Portrait of Kuka Parray

KUKA PARRAY

(A Pro Indian Militant)

AHMAD NAUSHAD

BLUEROSE PUBLISHERS
India | U.K.

Copyright © Ahmad Naushad 2023

All rights reserved by author. No part of this publication may be reproduced, stored in a retrieval system or transmitted in any form or by any means, electronic, mechanical, photocopying, recording or otherwise, without the prior permission of the author. Although every precaution has been taken to verify the accuracy of the information contained herein, the publisher assumes no responsibility for any errors or omissions. No liability is assumed for damages that may result from the use of information contained within.

BlueRose Publishers takes no responsibility for any damages, losses, or liabilities that may arise from the use or misuse of the information, products, or services provided in this publication.

For permissions requests or inquiries regarding this publication, please contact:

BLUEROSE PUBLISHERS
www.BlueRoseONE.com
info@bluerosepublishers.com
+91 8882 898 898
+4407342408967

ISBN: 978-93-5989-774-5

Cover design: Shivam
Typesetting: Namrata Saini

First Edition: November 2023

Contents

Chapter 1: Kashmir (A Flashback) 1

Chapter 2: Kumar 19

Chapter 3: Rashid Billa 52

Chapter 4: Fayaz Nawbadi 67

Chapter 5: Wafadar Khan 80

Chapter 6: Gh Rasool Parray aka Kaakh 86

Chapter 7: The Beginning of An End 101

Bibliography 135

Chapter 1

Kashmir (A Flashback)

Doctor just finished the checkup of my uncle and told us that we can go out for breakfast so me and my cousin (Armaan) planned to go out near Ali Jana medicate which is right outside of the SKIMS Soura hospital, (Srinagar) where you can find traditional places eateries for quick snacks and tea breaks. So we told our uncle "Take some rest by the time we will be back". Said **Arif**

We stepped outside and reached to a Restaurant.

Server: Assalamu Aalikum jinab bethiye aur hukum kijiye kya laavu aapke liye.

Siraaj: jinab 2 chai aur 2 patties de dijiye

Server: jinab abhi laaya

Siraaj: Zara jaldi kijiyega please, humara patient hai andar hospital main unko bhi breakfast karana hai.

Server: lo ji abhi leke aata hu

I was calmly sitting on couch and listening the conversation while scrolling down the news feed on internet.

Restaurant owner on cash desk: Waise jinab aap kahan se aaye hai aur mareez ko kya takleef hai?

Siraaj: ji hum Sopore se hai aur mere uncle ko kidney main takleef hai.

Restaurant owner: Allah aapke beemar uncle ko shifa de.

Aur aap miyan aap bhi Sopore se hai kya (mujhse poocha)

Arif: ji nhi, main Hajan se hun sopore se lagbag 20 kmr door hai.

Restaurant owner: Hajan, kahi aap KUKA PARRAY wale Hajan ki baat to nhi kar rhe hai?

The moment I heard the Name KUKA PARRAY I got slightly uncomfortable with the conversation now. Because this name was popular with some good and most of the bad reasons among Kashmir and in the whole Country. But I still calmed myself.

Arif: ji main ussi ki baat kar rha hu

Server: jinab, KUKA PARRAY, kon hai yeh aadmi jo aap itna darr darr ke bol rhe hain.

Restaurant Owner: Darr, Darr to kuch bhi nahi beta is naam se to maut bhi khauf khati hai.

Server: lagta hai jinaab aapki mulaqat huvi hai shayid unse.

Restaurant Owner: nahi maine to unko saamne kabhi nhi dekha lekin ek din unke aadmi jinko ikhwaan wale bolte hai woh mere ghar aaye, un logu ne 3 din mujhe mere kamre main ulta latka ke rakha aur meri biwi se khana banvake khate the. Mere ghr main jitney bhi zever aur naqad cash tha poora deke maine apni jaan bachayi.

Hajan, A town in north Kashmir's (earlier Baramulla now) Bandipora district which is known for its fertile land for Saints, Scholars, poets and literature, Where famous poet Wahaab parray Hajini, Prof. Mohi ud din Hajini, Asad Parray, Aziz Hajini, Gulzar Hajini, Molana Rashid Sahib, Molvi Sideequla, and many more scholars and poets were born. But now Hajan is popular and known In India with one name **KUKA PARRAY**.

Hajan has seen a lot of ups and downs and has played very important role in the history of Kashmir.

Before explaining further, we would go back to the root from where all of this started, without knowing the history future decisions always seems blur before bare eyes.

Indian was about to get rid from the British rule and form a country which had immense complications in its way despite which this responsibility was given to Sardar Vallabhai Patel and he did a tremendous job.

When the Britishers were leaving India, they had set some conditions to form the country, which was, It would be the wish of princely states whether they want to be with India, Pakistan or they want to stay independent.

There were 565 princely states who had already started to form two countries. From India side this responsibility was given to Sardar Vallabhai Patel as mentioned earlier. He was the Deputy Prime Minister of India and this was not an easy job to do. Law here says princely states should be asked on which side they want to be, but this is real world where many good and bad things happen and when it comes to form a country all right and wrong ways are followed, all methods were used to merge these small and big princely states and they were made to sign a document called as "Instrument of Accession".

Patel has done his job very nicely; all the princely states were merged with India but three places where this seemed to be very difficult was Junagarh, Hyderabad and Jammu and Kashmir.

Junagarh's population was mostly Hindu's and the king was Muslim he didn't want to join with India, He wanted to be with Pakistan. On September 15th 1947 he signed an agreement with Pakistan and merged with Pakistan. The rebellion was caused and the King of Junagarh fled to Pakistan. And when things were at peace a plebiscite was conducted. Plebiscite simply means people would vote which side they want to be.

When plebiscite was conducted about 99% of the voting were in the favor of being with India. One more important thing in this was when Britishers were leaving, they were holding the defense of both India and Pakistan in their hands. Both the commanders were Britishers which was good thing because if it were not like this than there would have been lot of disputes.

And now it was Hyderabad's turn. The King of Hyderabad was Muslim and also wanted to join Pakistan, but this was not practically possible as Hyderabad is situated in the middle. And second thing is that they had seen the condition in Junagarh's case, which terrified him, the king signed the agreement with Government of India. Which is also called "standstill agreement" which means now the things would remain as it is, after one year it will be decided to go with India or Pakistan.

Patel was happy with it because right now he had to focus on Jammu and Kashmir. Merger of Junagarh and Hyderabad with Pakistan was not practically possible that is why Pakistan faced a lot of problems. If these two states would have merged with Pakistan, they would have faced same problem like Bangladesh in future. But that was not the case with Jammu and Kashmir. Jammu and Kashmir shares its border with Pakistan and Jinnah had seen the plebiscite in Junagarh, He was very hopeful if plebiscite would happen in Kashmir's case, Then the decision will come in their favor as Kashmir was Muslim Majority state, with time Pakistan's obsession towards Kashmir was increasing. The king of Kashmir Hari Singh was a Hindu and the king did not want leave his throne at any cost. That's why whatever the options were in front of him, they were all the ones will all the problems. If king Hari Singh joins Pakistan, but Pakistan is an Islamic nation and that would be very difficult for a Hindu King to survive there. He knew this fact very well. If he joins India Nehru is always talking about democracy. Talking about conducting elections, if elections happen there, the majority is of Muslim he won't become a king anyways. King Hari Singh loved his throne very much. Even if he remains independent, everyone knew very well that whichever Princely states will come in the middle of two countries will face many problems. So it was very difficult for King Hari Singh to take the decision.

As time passed Pakistan's obsession Towards Kashmir kept increasing. The biggest problem for them was that their army was in the hands of the British so they could not attack Kashmir even if they wanted to.

Pakistan prepared an army of 10 thousand people who looked like civilians Called "Azaad Kashmir Fauj", which can attack Kashmir, this all was later accepted by Pakistan in the UN and is on paper.

When Hari Singh came to know about Azaad Kashmir Fauj, he was very sure that he will win very easily. His chief of army, Rajendra Singh Tried to Explain to him that the Muslims in our army can betray us and join Pakistan, but King Hari Singh did not have any other options left, after these people moved forward, the same thing happened which Rajender Singh was scared of. And they went out of control. When these people reached Baramulla, they caused so much destruction which those people have not forgotten till today. The way the defense of Pakistan was in the hands of the British, the same way, the defense of India was in the hands of the British as well.

Now India cannot make Azaad (independent) army in just a day, so they talked to Mountbatten. Mountbatten's Stance was very clear that they will not use their army to attack anyone. We will use our army on one condition only, if we were being attacked and we have to defend ourselves, and because Kashmir is not part of the India, so we cannot attack them. When Pakistan's army was just 50 kilometers away from Srinagar, King Hari Singh asked India for their help, India sent V.V. Menon to Hari Singh with one document.

Hari Singh singed the document and Kashmir became part of India. This document which was signed was the same document which was signed by the other princely states, when they joined India. When India started withdrawing its forces from one side, Pakistan also tried to withdraw its forces. They talked to the British who had the same answer that Mountbatten had given to India that Kashmir is not Part of India, if we land our forces now, then it will be considered as attack rather than defense. Jinnah was very furious about the agreement between Kashmir and India. He called Mountbatten and talked to him that they will not consider this agreement as when agreement was signed between Junagarh and Pakistan, the agreement was considered invalid and a plebiscite was conducted. Mountbatten had also given the same Indication that when there will be peace here, then here also, there will be plebiscite. After this, two things happened due to which India's stance became weak, the first thing is that Nehru announced on the stage that when the war will be over, there will be a plebiscite. And the second thing is that the war which was going on for one and half years, Nehru went to the United Nations (UN) to resolve these controversies. And those who were unhappy about Nehru going to UN were saying that the war was going on for more than a year and a half, it could have been extended a little bit more so that they could have taken the entire area rather than going to the UN.

The UN's resolution came, there were three points in that.

- The first point was that stay wherever you are and do not continue the fight further.
- The second point was that Pakistan's forces have to evacuate from Kashmir, and then India's forces will withdraw themselves.
- The third point was that when these two forces will get back then the citizens will decide whether they want to go Pakistan or India or they want to remain Independent. This means there will be voting there, a plebiscite will be conducted. Since then, till today the point which the fight has stopped is called LOC "line of Control" and the area in which there is Pakistan is called Pakistan Occupied Kashmir (POK) by India, and the area till where the India had covered is Called Indian Occupied Kashmir (IOK) by Pakistani Portals. And since then, till today there has been no permanent solution for it.

After that Kashmir had its own events going side by side, according to a timeline article published by "Adi Magazine"

In 1946 NC launches "Quit Kashmir" movement and MC starts a campaign of action; both are against the monarchy. Sheikh Abdullah and Chaudhary Ghulam Abbas are arrested. Over the years, Abdullah has grown closer to Indian Congress leaders and is opposed to Jinnah's Muslim League. Yet, he agrees Kashmir should remain its own entity. The Muslim Conference leans toward Jinnah.

In 1947 Between **August and October**, Kashmir is independent. With Pakistan now a reality, Jamaat Islamic activists want Kashmir to join Pakistan if it becomes an Islamic state, yet their parent body in British India has opposed Jinnah. Muslim Conference passes a resolution to join Pakistan. The Socialist Party also wants to join Pakistan. But NC is opposed to the idea. The British withdrawal and the partition of British India into India and Pakistan leads to violence in Bengal, Delhi, Punjab and elsewhere. Kashmiris have been fighting against the monarchy and don't see their struggle as part of South Asian secular, Hindu, or Muslim nationalisms, but the British ask "Princely Rulers" to accede either to India or to Pakistan based on geographical contiguity and religious demography. According to this Partition logic, Kashmir should have gone to Pakistan, as the state has a close to 77 percent Muslim population. In **September and October 1947**, Hindu militias and Dogra troops attack Jammu's Muslims, killing tens of thousands. In Poonch, along the border with newly-created Pakistan, rebels create an independent state called "Azad (Free) Jammu Kashmir (AJK)." As ethnic cleansing of Jammu Muslims continues, many flee to AJK and to Pakistan. Much of Muslim Conference leadership and members are displaced. According to census reports from the time and later research, upwards of 200,000 Muslims are dead and an equal number become refugees. After what will come to be known as the "Jammu Massacre," Jammu becomes a Hindu-majority city. Meanwhile, the Dogras lose control of Gilgit Baltistan province in the north. With their leader, Sheikh Abdullah, in prison, NC remains dormant. In **September**, troops from the neighboring state of Patiala and Hindu nationalist paramilitaries of the RSS arrive to bolster the Dogras. Pakistan blocks supplies into Kashmir. Indian Congress leaders put pressure on the Dogras to accede to India and release Abdullah. The Dogra maharaja wants to remain independent and has signed a Standstill Agreement with Pakistan, but India has refused to sign. As rebellion continues along the borders, on **October 22, 1947**, members of Afridi and other Pashtun groups begin to converge along the border and enter Baramulla to aid Kashmiris but falter without any clear leadership. The Maharaja flees the Kashmir valley and asks India for help. Indians demand he sign the Treaty of Accession and give power over Kashmir's defence, foreign affairs, and communication to India. Abdullah is made Emergency Administrator and he sees Pashtuns as a threat. On **October 26,** Indian troops arrive in Srinagar and the next day Maharaja signs the treaty. Indian invasion pulls Pakistani troops in too. The first India-Pakistan war over Kashmir breaks out. On **November 21**, Nehru says: "I have repeatedly stated that as soon as peace and order have been established; Kashmir should decide about accession by plebiscite or referendum under international auspices such as those of United Nations."

In 1948 By the middle of the year, the war has entered a stalemate. India takes the case of Kashmir to the United Nations. Kashmir is officially recognized as a disputed territory. The United Nations Security Council passes a resolution (UNSC Resolution 47) providing for 1. Ceasefire, 2. Withdrawal of Pakistani and Indian troops, and 3. Plebiscite in Kashmir (under international supervision with minimal Indian military presence). UN Commission on India and Pakistan (UNCIP) is created.

In 1949 Ceasefire is proclaimed under the UN auspices. India is in control of two-thirds of the historic Kashmir state while Pakistan has control over one-third, including the AJK.

In 1950 India backtracks on its promise of the plebiscite, even though Nehru would continue to make statements about India's pledge to Kashmiris until 1959. Indian Constitution comes into effect and Article 1 proclaims the entire state of J&K as a part of the territory of India. Article 370 gives a "special" status to the State of J&K, more or less corresponding to the terms of the Instrument of Accession. Pro-Pakistan Kashmiri leaders are arrested, and many are sent into exile.

In 1951 Elections are held in the state. The UNSC passes a resolution (UNSC Resolution 91) saying elections will not be a substitute for the plebiscite. Sheikh Abdullah wins the elections, mostly unopposed, and becomes the Prime Minister. Abdullah carries out land reforms and adopts measures such as debt relief. The Jammu Kashmir

Constituent Assembly is created to draft the constitution for the state. In India, Hindu nationalists begin agitation over giving special status to Kashmir. They demand "one country, one constitution, one flag."

In 1952 Land reforms, while benefitting impoverished Kashmiri Muslims and under-caste Hindus, lead to resentment among erstwhile members of Dogra royalty and Hindu feudal, who assemble under the aegis of a Hindu nationalist party, Praja Parishad. Abdullah sees them as a threat but is unable to control their influence. He begins to shift positions between endorsing Kashmir's accession to India and supporting the right of self-determination for Kashmiris. He signs the Delhi Agreement, but does not confirm the accession of Kashmir to India. The Delhi Agreement says: 1. except in three matters listed under Instrument of Accession, sovereignty will reside in Jammu and Kashmir; 2. Kashmiris will be citizens of India, but the elected Kashmir government will decide permanent residency requirements in the state; 3. Kashmir will have its own flag and constitution; 4. Kashmir will have a Prime Minister (*wazir azam*) and President (*sadr-e-riyasat*). Jamaat Islami separates from its parent body in India.

In 1953 As Hindu nationalist groups coalesce against Abdullah, the Indian government claims he is conspiring with the Chinese, the Arabs, and the Americans to create an independent Kashmir. In **August**, Abdullah is arrested (he will spend the next decade in prison). One of his aides and the deputy prime minister until then, G.M. Bakshi, is installed as the Prime Minister. Abdullah's loyalists are removed from the government and the NC.

In 1954 Bakshi gets the accession formally ratified in 1954. India passes a "Presidential Order" using Article 370 which effectively gives the Indian parliament many more powers than were part of the Instrument of Accession and the Delhi Agreement. This is the start of the "erosion of autonomy," which will continue in the years to come. All dissent in Kashmir is crushed.

In 1955 Afzal Beg, a lieutenant of Abdullah's, forms the Plebiscite Front, which becomes the principal opposition to the governments led by India-loyalist Bakshi and his successors.

In 1956 The J&K Constituent Assembly adopts a new constitution, declaring the state an integral part of the Indian Union. Kashmiri activists, including those from Plebiscite Front, reject the declaration, and continue to insist on the promised self-determination.

In 1957 The UN passes another resolution (UNSC Resolution 122) affirming that only the "will of the people expressed through the democratic method of a free and impartial plebiscite conducted under the auspices of the United Nations" will determine Kashmir's final status, and states that the J&K Constituent Assembly's actions, including administrative or legal changes, are invalid and would not constitute a final disposition of the state.

In 1962 India and China fight a war. India loses control over large tracts of land in Ladakh, especially Aksai Chin, that had been part of the State of Jammu and Kashmir.

In 1963 A holy relic—believed to be a strand of hair from the Prophet's beard—is found missing from the Hazratbal shrine in Srinagar. Popular agitation erupts across Kashmir Valley and continues until the relic is mysteriously recovered in January 1964. Protests expand against extension of Indian powers to Kashmir including Indian president's power to dismiss Kashmiri governments.

In 1965 Second India-Pakistan war breaks out after Pakistan sends infiltrators across the ceasefire line in August. The war ends in a ceasefire on **September 23**. The status quo remains. India removes the title of Prime Minister and Sadr e Riyasat from its loyalist Kashmiri officials, instead using the term Chief Minister.

In 1966 Small Kashmiri armed revolutionary groups emerge, some in the shadow of the Plebiscite Front. These groups call for complete independence of Jammu and Kashmir. One of these groups is Jammu Kashmir National Liberation Front (JKNLF) created by Maqbool Bhat and others. Another is Al Fatah, which builds a strong underground network. Most are arrested and will spend years in prison.

In 1971 India and Pakistan fight a war, resulting in the secession of East Pakistan and the formation of Bangladesh.

In 1972 India and Pakistan sign the Shimla Agreement, which recognizes the ceasefire line of 1949 as the Line of Control (LoC). The Shimla Agreement includes a clause stating that the final settlement of Kashmir will be decided bilaterally. Kashmiris see themselves as being further sidelined in future negotiations over their own country.

In 1974 Sheikh Abdullah is allowed to return to Kashmir. Many Kashmiris welcome him. But on Indira Gandhi's insistence, he disbands the Plebiscite Front. Abdullah agrees to give up the demand for self-determination.

In 1975 Abdullah accepts the much diminished position of Chief Minister. In **June**, Prime Minister Indira Gandhi plunges India into an Emergency. Abdullah supports her and does not oppose when the Emergency is extended to Kashmir ten days later. Abdullah and his aide Beg win by-elections, but Syed Ali Geelani, who is a Jamaat Islami legislator, claims election rigging. Abdullah bans Jamaat Islami and closes down dozens of its schools across Kashmir. Revolutionary armed groups that had risen in the shadow of the Plebiscite Front are in a disarray, even though Abdullah drops long-standing cases against Al Fatah members.

In 1976 Maqbool Bhat, having spent years in Indian and Pakistani jails (in Pakistan, for being suspected as an Indian spy), is arrested again in Kashmir, where a death warrant has earlier been issued against him for the murder of a bank official at the hands of one of his associates.

On **May 29, 1977** Amanullah Khan, Abdul Khaliq Ansari and few others from the Azad Kashmiri diaspora in Britain form the Jammu Kashmir Liberation Front (JKLF) in Birmingham. Maqbool Bhat is proclaimed to have joined the new organization. Sheikh Abdullah wins elections in 1977. With the Indian establishment's backing, the opposition to his NC is decimated. The old Jamaat Islami, having contested the elections since 1971, wins only one seat in the Assembly.

In 1979 Iran's Islamic revolution and the execution of Pakistan's former Prime Minister, Z.A. Bhutto, on the orders of General Zia ul Haq, causes widespread ripples across Kashmir. Jamaat Islami members, seen as supporters of General Zia, are attacked by NC cadres as well as by some Islamic preachers in the countryside, especially in Islamabad (Anantnag) where Jamaat Islami's support among the salaried classes is growing.

On 1982 **September 8**, Sheikh Abdullah dies.

In 1983 Massive election rigging creates dissensions within NC and conflicts begin among Abdullah's heirs. Indian PM Indira Gandhi, campaigning in Jammu, ignites Hindu passions against Kashmiri Muslims.

In 1984 On **February 11**, Maqbool Bhat is hanged in Tihar Jail. Indian authorities refuse to return his body to his family. Small groups of Kashmiris cross the LoC to plan armed movement and return to form underground cells. In **April**, the Indian Army captures the Siachen Glacier region of Kashmir from Pakistan. In **June**, the Indian military's assault on the Golden Temple, the spiritual center of Sikhs in Amritsar, leaves hundreds of Sikhs dead. Many Sikh activists cross the Punjab border into Pakistan to get arms training. In **July**, the Indian governor in Kashmir openly interferes in Kashmiri politics. Farooq, Abdullah's son and heir, is dismissed as the Chief Minister and his opponent in the NC and brother-in-law, Ghulam Muhammad Shah, is installed in his place. Small new Islamist groups begin to emerge in Kashmir, mostly led by Kashmir University students. In **October**, Indira Gandhi is shot dead by her bodyguards.

In 1986 Mujahideen war against the Soviets in Afghanistan is at its peak. India loyalist and Farooq Abdullah's brother in law, Ghulam Muhammad Shah, is dismissed as Chief Minister, after Farooq gives assurances to Indian PM Rajiv Gandhi that he will crack down on the growing unrest in Kashmir. Farooq forms a coalition government with the Indian National Congress in Kashmir.

In 1987 a number of opposition parties join to form an alliance against the NC. They are called the Muslim United Front (MUF). There is blatant poll rigging. Young polling agents of MUF, among them Yasin Malik, are arrested and tortured. Farooq Abdullah is allowed to win the elections and becomes Chief Minister. The MUF wins only four seats—despite a clear wave of support for the party—including one by Syed Ali Geelani of the Jamaat Islami and Qazi Nisar, the Mirwaiz (head preacher) of South Kashmir. MUF contestants, like Yusuf Shah, are arrested.

In 1986 Farooq Abdullah was elected chief minister of Jammu and Kashmir and he continued the rule till 1990. Besides militancy had started growing roots in Kashmir especially north Kashmir was the hotspot.

Militancy was growing at full pace throughout Kashmir, the most popular organizations JKLF later Hizbul Mujahideen had almost taken over Kashmir.

During 1990 Farooq Abdullah had resigned and now Jammu Kashmir was in Governor rule and one big incident happened which is also known as biggest unfortunate incident happened to Kashmiri pandits and Kashmiri Muslims which divided both the communities ever. Its said that almost 90% of Kashmiri pandits left their home land to save their life. There are certain estimates by scholars and other organizations that almost 228 Kashmiri pandits were killed in few days.

Now Kashmir was under full Control of Militants, Indian Army was helpless to tackle with the situation because they couldn't figure out how many civilians are involved. There were hundreds of civilians killed by Indian army and militants.

Indian Army would sometimes kill people doubting them to be OGW (over ground workers).

Militants would kill same civilians doubting them to be Army Informers, on both the sides Kashmiri people were getting killed on uncountable speed. Now India was losing Kashmir day by day and they could not figure out any possible solutions for the problem. In 1989

Chapter 2

Kumar

The prime minister called the meeting as the situation in Kashmir was getting worse day by day even Indian army seemed to be helpless.

Prime minister: call the RAW Chief immediately, tell him to meet as soon as possible.

PA: yes sir, calling right away.

PA calls RAW chief on hotline

PA on phone: good morning, sir PM wants to see you immediately in his office.

RAW Chief: yes, sure I will be there as soon as possible.

PM: Get me all the officers in my office tomorrow 10:00am.

PA calls all the high officials for the meeting

Next day:

RAW Chief, Indian Army Chief and other officers arrive at the PM office for the meeting.

PM: do we have any solution here, why is Kashmir getting off our hand's day by day, what seems to be so tough here just 500 militants have overtaken Kashmir while when more than 6 lakh soldiers are there.

Indian Army Chief: Sir it's not just five hundred militants Civilians are also involved and we don't know how many. So, whenever we go for an encounter, the civil causalities are more than militants which we cannot afford every day.

PM: so, you trying to say 6 lakh soldiers cannot do anything.

Indian Army Chief: sir we can do a lot but there would be countless civil causalities that is the only problem here.

PM: does anyone have any plan?

RAW Chief: sir, as per our Sources, north Kashmir is the most affected area as compared to south Kashmir. And among all militants, there is one man who is most dangerous among all who has the most influence among people and who has been untraceable after hundreds of search operations conducted by the Indian Army.

PM: go on

RAW Chief: sir, the man I am talking about is not only well-trained militant but a commander and often hides in his hometown, Hajan, it's a village in district Baramulla where he has local support and that's why he is been very difficult to trace.

PM: who is this man you talking about

RAW Chief: PARRAY the commander of JKLF.

PM: get every detail on him and meet me in my office tomorrow at 02:00 pm

RAW Chief: yes sir.

PM: meeting dispersed.

Here in Kashmir encounters were on, blood on streets everywhere, whole Kashmir had become a battle field. There wasn't a single day without a killing. militancy was on peak and day by day rising local support and civilians joining militant outfits was a new normal now.

Next day PM office

Now PM called only RAW chief and some of his high command officers because now what was going to happen nobody could have ever imagined, it was going to change the fate of Kashmir and the whole India forever.

Whoever was called had arrived to PM office.

PM to PA: has everyone arrived

PA: Yes, sir everyone you asked me to call is already here waiting for you in meeting room.

PM arrives in meeting room.

All officers in room: good morning, sir

PM: good morning officers

RAW Chief: Sir as you asked, we are ready with every possible information about KUKAPARRAY.

PM: ok Tell me what all we know about this man.

Raw chief with his presentation on projector screen displays some of the images of KUKA PARRAY and his associates.

RAW CHIEF: Sir the man we are talking about his MOHAMMAD YOUSUF PARRAY alias **KUKA PARRAY** he is from north Kashmir's Baramulla district; the village is called HAJAN which is known for poets and scholars and it is the biggest town in north Kashmir with large population.

If we start from beginning the man we are talking about was a Shepherd in 80's and would always roam with his sheep in near local forest area, this is a large forest range of willow trees surrounding the Wular lake from Bandipora connects to Hajan and goes till Baramulla, almost 40 kms in range. Please note this because this whole forest range is very important here.

PM: go on

RAW CHIEF: Sir this man KUKA PARRAY a shepherd turns into a poet with the pen name **JAMSHEED SHEERAZI,** as I mentioned earlier this place is known to create poets and Scholars so he becomes one, after becoming poet he also formed a local group of folk singers and started to perform in different occasions in different parts of Kashmir, and this is when he gathered all the popularity and influence among the locals. And I must say he was very popular and successful.

PM: so what went wrong here.

RAW CHIEF: sir the story starts here. Being so popular in Kashmir is not a good thing because it attracts a lot of attention.

Getting lot of attention among locals he also was noticed by pro Pakistani militants in Kashmir who were very less in numbers active in Kashmir.

So, after getting in touch with the them they were able to brain wash him and convinced him to join the militant ranks.

They did not make him join directly in Kashmir, they sent him to Pakistan for arms training and he did not return as a normal militant when he came back, he was already a COMMANDER with hundreds of his associates.

So now the problem is being so popular in Kashmir he has civilian support which makes it more difficult to trace him or neutralize him.

Army has searched all villages every day, they would search and cordon off the areas but nothing was found, he always escapes with his local support.

There is not a single house in his local area HAJAN where Army has not searched for him, but nothing as always. Even if he is traced civilians come between him and army which makes It hard to catch him because army cannot open fire on civilians.

And Sir this is the very guy responsible for Kashmir's current situation he doesn't allow people to vote he kills the people who try to stand or contest for elections. The previous politicians have left Kashmir, some are in other Indian states, some are abroad; nobody dares to come back.

Army cannot interfere directly because that would result in countless civilian causalities and can attract international news attention. Then human rights, UN official all would be behind us which makes it more tough to handle.

PM: Are you trying to say we are losing Kashmir; no, we cannot afford that at any cost. Do whatever is possible, i want to revoke democracy In Kashmir and conduct election we have to show to international communities that Kashmir is peaceful and happy with India. We have so many agencies so many officers do we have not a single person who can make this possible.

RAW CHIEF: yes, sir we have one. An officer who is known for these kinds of operations who has done something no one could do for India alone.

PM: who are you talking about.

RAW CHIEF: KUMAR,

PM: are you talking about same Kumar who just exposed Pakistan's nuclear test and who has done fantastic job in north east and Kerala like situations.

RAW CHIEF: Yes, sir I am talking about the same officer.

PM: go on I trust him too.

RAW CHIEF: sir for this operation which is going to be highly confidential, I would need some extra powers and authority and off course support from Army chief in Kashmir.

PM: don't you worry about that I will inform the Army chief in Kashmir personally about it. You go for it I need Kashmir back in anyhow.

PM: Meeting dispersed.

Kashmir was in total chaos, Encounters, protests and conflicts between Indian Army and civilians was a new normal. The most affected area was north Kashmir particularly Hajan and adjoining areas. Meanwhile Raw and PM were worried about it and hoping that normalcy will return one day.

After some days RAW CHIEF meets Kumar and discussed the plan with him where KUMAR asked for some of the special requests and powers to handle it which was of course provided by RAW CHIEF and PM office.

RAW CHIEF: Kumar, are you sure you can do this? The whole country is counting on us. though they won't get to know you, but believe me we are counting on you.

KUMAR: I am sure sir, i will try my best and trust me I got this.

RAW CHIEF: you have my all support but be very careful the place you are going to be in is more dangerous than Pakistan these days. And remember you are our last hope.

KUMAR: I understand sir.

RAW CHIEF: come on let's do this.

KUMAR leaves for Kashmir next day which he knew is a place overrun by chaos, encounters and protests but he was a smart man he had recently exposed Pakistan's nuclear test and now he was the perfect man for India to deal with Kashmir like situation.

Kumar secretly had his meetings in Kashmir with top officials regarding the plan and he just disappeared in crowd which was his specialty.

Now Indian Army was working as their routines everything look liked a barren land with rubble of houses destroyed bridges and a fear in the air, this was the present picture of Kashmir which was once called the heaven on earth.

Here in north Kashmir popularity of KUKA PARRAY was growing simultaneously among the locals especially in his town HAJAN, which is a town of 32 other small villages. KUKA PARRAY had almost 25 – 45 other militant associates with him all time. Army would continuously search the villages but would get nothing because of the popularity KUKAPARRAY had gained and support locals were giving.

It has been months now KUMAR did nothing but kept an eye on the moments of KUKA PARRAY and his associates, tried to meet some of them but nothing would work until finally he got in touch with his one of the ground workers whose name was ABDUL REHMAN PARRAY aka **DILAWAR.**

KUMAR started friendship with Dilawar in a hope that one day KUKA will come to meet DILAWAR and he will get his chance which he has been waiting for months but DILAWAR did not let him meet KUKA easily he tried to cut the conversation whenever KUMAR tried to get information about him. But finally, KUMAR convinced DILAWAR that if he takes him to KUKA, he will give anything DILAWAR asks for. This was the exact time when Kashmir was going to change forever. Till now a lot had happened in recent years.

- 1989 when RABIYA SAYED daughter of MUFTI MOHAMMAD SAYED was kidnapped by same outfit which KUKA belonged that was JKLF (Jammu Kashmir liberation front)
- 1990 when exodus of Kashmiri pandits started and they were getting killed day by day, it was not only Kashmiri pandits which were getting targeted but Muslims too, though Muslims were in majority in Kashmir still they were equally effected.
- It's said that almost 90% of Kashmiri pandits left their home land to save their life. There are certain estimates that almost 228 Kashmiri pandits were killed in few days.

After the exodus of Kashmiri pandits and the failure of almost every formed government in Kashmir, Kashmir was under full Control of Militants. Indian Army was helpless to tackle with the situation because they couldn't figure out how many civilians are involved. It was almost impossible to figure out that how this growing pace of militancy and the influence among people for them can be controlled. There were hundreds of civilians killed by Indian army and militants.

Indian Army would sometimes kill people doubting them to be OGW (over ground workers).

Militants would kill same civilians doubting them to be Army Informers, on both sides Kashmiri people were getting killed at uncountable speed.

One day finally DILAWAR took KUMAR to meet KUKA in his local area and set a meeting for dinner where DILAWAR had already told KUKA about him. KUMAR introduced himself to KUKA as Govt Official who has come to meet KUKA PARRAY for peace and about the situation in Kashmir. Now that KUMAR had hi hello with him so he kept pushing to meet him often where he slowly tried to take all the information from KUKA about the reason why they have been fighting with Army and why they formed this militant outfit.

KUMAR: Parray Sahab aap se kuch poochu bura to nhi manenge.

KUKA: ji poocheye kya poochna chahte hai aap.

KUMAR: waise poochna kuch nhi chahta bas samajna chahta hun k aap aur aapki jo yeh tanzeem hai JKLF aap chahte kya hai aakhir. Apne hi mulk main jung karke kya fayda milega kisiko.

KUKA: Ab jung hai to hai aur aapke mulk ke saath hai hamare mulk ke saath nhi.

KUMAR: kya app INDIA ko apna mulk nhi maante.

KUKA: konse mulk ki baat kar rahe hai aap, woh mulk jisne kashmiriyun ka khoon paani ki tarah bahaya hai, jisne help karne ke bahane Kashmir pe hi kabza kara. Hindustan se ab azaadi lene se ab hame koi nhi rok sakta.

KUMAR: jinaab aap, aap to gussa hogaye main to aise pooch raha tha.

KUKA: aap kya chahte hai hum Hindustan ko apna mulk kahe, gale lagaye Hindustan ko, agar aisa hai to woh kabhi nhi hosakta.

KUMAR: to aap keh rahe hai k aap hindustaan se alag hoke Pakistan ke saath rehna chahte hai. Lekin maanf kijijye muje bataye Pakistan Kashmir ko sambalne ke halat main hain bi, kya desakta hai Pakistan aapko aur Kashmir ko.

KUKA: kuch dega ya nhi dega lekin hamesh hamare saath khada rehta hai, Hindustan ke jaise peeth pe churra nhi chalata. Aap nhi samaj sakte kitni takleef di hai hame Hindustan ne.

Waise hamara Maqsad Pakistan se milna nhi Kashmir Ki Azaadi hai, inshallah

KUMAR: aisi baat nhi hai Hindustan ne hmaesha aapko apna samja hai aur Hindustan aapke liye bahut kuch kar bhi sakta hai.

KUKA: itni takleef di hai itna khoon bhahaya woh kaafi nhi hai ab kya karega.

KUMAR: jinaab main to asie hi pooch rha tha, mujhe umeed hai aap humse dosti nhi todenge ab. Hahaha

KUKA: aapse ladai karke hame kya milega hamari jung to poore Hindustan ke nizam se hai.

Meanwhile Indian army conducted a search operation next day in the area near Hajan where 2 of the militants were killed and a lot of arms and ammunition were recovered which made militants to hide out in nearby areas. KUKA also went underground for some days.

Army was continuously looking for KUKA PARRAY so they could neutralize him and weak JKLF in Kashmir because KUKA was the most dreaded militant among all.

Kashmir had recently seen multiple incident which could be called beyond normal some of the incidents in recent times were:

In 1987 a number of opposition parties joined to form an alliance against the NC. They are called the Muslim United Front (MUF). There is blatant poll rigging. Young polling agents of MUF, among them Yasin Malik, are arrested and tortured. Farooq Abdullah is allowed to win the elections and becomes Chief Minister. The MUF wins only four seats—despite a clear wave of support for the party—including one by Syed Ali Geelani of the Jamaat Islami and Qazi Nisar, the Mirwaiz (head preacher) of South Kashmir. MUF contestants, like Yusuf Shah, are arrested.

In 1988 Repression in Kashmir increases. Protestors demanding basic things, like electricity, are shot down. Several groups of young Kashmiri men, including Hamid Sheikh, Ashfaq Wani, Javaid Mir, and Yasin Malik (now out of jail), cross the LoC for arms training. Later known as the HAJY group (acronym of the first letters of their names), they join the JKLF. Busy fighting the Soviets in Afghanistan, Pakistan however sends them back without promises. Pakistan cuts even minimal support as General Zia dies in a crash and Benazir Bhutto becomes the prime minister, who invites Indian PM Rajiv Gandhi to Pakistan. JKLF declare armed struggle against India, exploding several small bombs in Srinagar. Jamaat Islami opposes armed struggle in its publication *Azan* and insists on the 1985 amendment to its party constitution that calls for resolution through constitutional means and dialogue.

In 1989 the judge who had sentenced Maqbool Bhat to death is shot dead. Indian operations to capture JKLF members become intense. Hamid Sheikh has been captured. In November and December, JKLF successfully uses a high-profile kidnapping to negotiate the release of their members, including Sheikh. Vast crowds of Kashmiris come out in support of JKLF and to welcome the rebels. With Soviet withdrawal from Afghanistan, Pakistan turns attention to Kashmir, but seems interested in creating its own group, one that could profess a pro-Pakistan ideology. Among several such groups, Hizbul Mujahideen (HM) is founded by a Jamaat

Islami activist and schoolteacher known as Master Ahsan Dar. Yusuf Shah, also from Jamaat Islami, joins the HM.

In 1990 Indian military forces carry out several massacres across Kashmir in January. Protests intensify, and thousands of Kashmiris publicly resign from pro-India parties. The four MUF legislators resigned as well. On January 17, India dismisses Farooq Abdullah's government and imposes central rule. A Hindu nationalist bureaucrat, Jagmohan, is installed as the governor. He claims that "Kashmir is sick, and I am its nursing orderly," and ominously threatens Kashmiris. Jagmohan swiftly launches widespread military crackdowns on urban neighbourhoods. Intense curfews are imposed. Armed groups carry out assassinations of government officials, NC activists, and intelligence agents. While many of these (~200) are Kashmiri Muslim, a significant number (~70) are Kashmiri Hindus, who have held top positions in the government and constitute three percent of the population. Thousands of Hindu families leave Kashmir on January 19 and head to Jammu in the south. (Years later, many Hindus would claim they left because they were afraid for their lives and that militant groups had threatened them, while many Kashmiri Muslims would blame Jagmohan for convincing Hindus to leave, facilitating their journey, and telling them they would be back after the winter when the rebellion was crushed in the Valley. According to Indian government sources, between 1989 and 2004, 219 Kashmiri Hindus were killed by armed militants, and one since then, while about 165,000 Hindus left Kashmir.)

On January 21, an estimated 55-65 unarmed protesters are killed by Indian troops near Gawakadal in Srinagar. Later that day, Jagmohan imposes a long curfew and a military siege leading to widespread misery in the middle of an icy winter. On January 25, Indian forces kill 21 protestors in Handwara town. On March 1, Indian soldiers kill around 50 Kashmiri protestors near Tengpora in Srinagar. In early March, an estimated one million Kashmiris take to the streets for several days. Indian soldiers kill dozens. On March 30, JKLF chief commander Ashfaq Wani is killed during an attack. Considered the main architect of the armed struggle, his death is the first big blow to the movement. Tens of thousands attend his funeral. Hundreds of young Kashmiris cross the LoC and return to join the JKLF. HM also recruits several activists. While the JKLF professes to be "secular" and wants "unification and independence" of Kashmir, the HM professes to be an "Islamic" organization with the goal of Kashmir's "merger with Pakistan." On May 21, an estimated million people attend the funeral march of the slain chief preacher of Kashmir, Mirwaiz Maulvi Farooq. An HM activist is blamed for the assassination. Some Kashmiris claim that the HM activist had been released from prison for this purpose. Indian paramilitaries kill 60 mourners and injured 200 near Hawal in Srinagar. Thousands of armed Kashmiris return from AJK training camps and enjoy widespread public support. Indian government replaces Jagmohan with Girish Saxena as the governor. India continues to send troops into the region. There are more than 300,000 active duty Indian soldiers in Kashmir now.

By summer, India imposes the Armed Forces Special Powers Act, which gives a free hand to the military.

In 1991 as repression continues, armed groups in Kashmir proliferate. JKLF is still the most prominent, but HM, the favourite of Pakistan, has now more trained cadres, better weapons, and has been adopted by Jamaat Islami as its armed wing. The Indian military is unable to crush the rebellion. Thousands of Kashmiris are dying in the war. On February 23, Indian soldiers enter two villages in north Kashmir, Kunan and Poshpora, and rape dozens of Kashmiri women. Indian government denies the charge. (Later, a Press Council of India committee would declare the women to be lying, but Kashmiri activists would argue the PCI committee hadn't even met the victims.)

In 1992 HM starts to gain more recruits in the countryside, especially where Jamaat Islami influence is predominant. HM ranks—now in thousands—are also filled by Afghan war veterans and Pakistanis. JKLF is still influential, but its main commanders are either dead or in prison. Yasin Malik, its second chief commander, has been in prison since 1990. Tensions between JKLF and HM grow as HM seeks dominance. Master Ahsan Dar is expelled from HM by now Pakistan-based Syed Salahuddin because of Dar's criticism of HM's attacks on the JKLF. Dar forms a smaller group named Muslim Mujahideen. Half a million Indian forces are deployed in the Kashmir Valley during this period. Prominent Kashmiri human rights activist and trade unionist H. N. Wanchoo is shot dead.

- January 1990: Jagmohan was appointed Governor. Farooq Abdullah resigned.
- 20 January 1990: An estimated 100 people were killed when a large group of unarmed protesters were fired upon by Indian troops at the Gawkadal bridge. This incident provoked an insurgency by the entire population.
- 1 March 1990: An estimated one million took to the streets and more than 40 people were killed in police firing.
- 13 February 1990: Lassa Kaul, director of Srinagar Doordarshan, was killed by the militants for implementing pro-Indian media policy.
- February 1990 – March 1990: Though the JKLF tried to explain that the killings of Pandits were not communal, the murders caused a scare among the minority Hindu community. The rise of new militant groups and unexplained killings of members of the community contributed to an atmosphere of insecurity for the Kashmiri Pandits. Joint reconciliation efforts by members from Muslim and Pandit communities were actively discouraged by Jagmohan.
- The popular name who started killing Kashmiri pandits was BITTA KARATE a militant who killed Satish Kumar tikku on instructions given by ISHFAQ MAJID WANI as per Bitta karate. He killed many people including Kashmiri pandita's and Muslims.

- 1990 – present: An officially estimated 10,000 Kashmiri youths crossed into Pakistan for training and procurement of arms. Indigenous and foreign militant groups besides pro-India renegade militants proliferated through the 1990s with an estimated half a million Indian security forces deployed in the Kashmir Valley. Increasing violence and human right violations by all sides led to tens of thousands of civilian casualties.

After all this chaos it was now more important for KUMAR to stop the ongoing riots and control the situation because it had been years now when election had been conducted. Due to high local support militants were very tough to trace and more and more civilians were joining militant ranks. Which was itself a sign that Kashmir slipping of India's hands.

After a month KUMAR got an opportunity to meet DILAWAR and motivated him to conduct a meeting again with KUKA where DILAWAR said he will try to meet KUKA and will try to speak to him as Army search operations are going everywhere.

During search operation they (ARMY) came to my (writer's) house one day and started throwing things here and there, don't know what their duty dog smelled in one of our rooms they started digging the floor which was made of concrete and left our house like a storm had passed.

DILAWAR met KUKA next day and told him about KUMAR, KUKA asked what does he want, he said he is top official of Indian Govt wants to talk about peace in Kashmir and has some deal to offer as well, I think we should meet him replied DILAWAR. Ok tell him to meet me at my home this Sunday evening said KUKA.

Next Sunday KUMAR arrived at Parray Mohalla Hajan KUKA PARRAY's residence in evening after some time KUKA also arrived with some of his associates.

Kumar and Dilawar were waiting in a room and Parray entered

KUKA: kaise hai Kumar sahab, Sunna hai aap ajkal hame bahut yaad karte hai.

KUMAR: ab aap hai hi yaad karne layak to kya kare.

KUKA: waise bhi aapke mulk ki poori Army bhi ajkal hame kuch zyada hi yaad kar rhi hai. Jagah jagah hame talash kar rhi hai.

KUMAR: ji woh sab to chalta hi rehta Army ka kaam hai.

KUKA: Lekin unse kehdijiye hum unke haath kabhi nhi aane wale KUKA ko pakadna itna asaan nhi hai. Hum Hindustan ko majboor kardenge Kashmir chodne ke liye ek din Inshallah. Khair aap bataye hum aapke liye kuch karsakte hai, hum waise yahan nhi aate aise halaat main Lekin Dilawar ne bola k kuch zaroori kaam hai aapko humse to maine socha dekhta hu k itna kya zaroori kaam hain aapko humse.

KUMAR: betheye to sahi batate hai araam se.

KUKA sits down accompanied with some of his men.

KUMAR: agar aap bura na mane to main aapse akele main kuch baat karna chahta hun.

KUKA to his men: sab log zara bahar hamara intizaar karo, main aata hu

Now Kumar, Kuka and Dilawar are only ones in room.

KUMAR: Parray sahab main aapke saath kuch baat karna chahta hun aapke tanzeem aur Kashmir ke halaat ke baare main. Actually, main aapke saath is masle ka hal chahta hu hamesha ke liye agar aap hamara saath de to.

KUKA: Hamara saath matlab, aapko yahan kisne beja hai, kon hai jisko hamare saath ki itni bekaraari hai.

KUMAR: Aise bolu to main is waqt Hindustan ki baat kar rha hu.

KUKA: Apko hum apna dost samjte hai isliye kuch nhi bol rhe hai, yeh baat kisi aur ne ki hoti to is waqt uski laash hamare saamne padi hoti.

Hindustan se hamara koi wasta nhi is mulk ko to hum apne pairu main layenge inshaallah. Hindustaan se hamara Azadi lene ka maqsad zaroor poora hoga aur hum karenge isko poora.

KUMAR: Main aapki baat aur apke jazbaat se sehmat hu, par mujhe ek baat zara samjaye k Hindustan se Azaad hone ke baad kasie rahega Kashmir is baat pe kabhi goar kiya hai apne.

KUKA: Kaise rahenge matlb jaise baaki azad mulk rehte hai waise rahenge aur yeh jihaad tab tak jaari rahega jabtak hum Hindustan se azaadi nhi lete.

KUMAR: Aur Pakistan woh kya aapko lagta hai chup bethega aapki azadi ke baad, aapko kya lagta woh aapko is waqt kyu itna support kar rha hai.

KUKA: Kyunki aapke Hindustan ne hame gulaam banake rakha hai kashmiriyu ko marte hai aaye hai saalu se.

KUMAR: Aisa bilkul nhi hai haa manta hu kuch hadisaat huve hai lekin yakeen maniye hindustaan Kashmir se bahut pyaar karta hai, shaan hai aap hamari.

KUKA: Agar waisa hota to aap kabhi humko aise gulamu ki tarah nhi rakhte yahan aam logun se zyada apki army dekhne ko milti hai, agar kisi ne zara si awaaz uthayi to usse army wale uthake kahan leke jaate hai kuch pata nhi chalta aur aap kehte hai k Hindustan Kashmir se bahut pyaar karta hai.

KUMAR: ji main aapki har ek baat se itifaq rakhta hu, aur isi masla ka hal yakeen maniye main bhi chahta hu.

KUKA: acha aap iss masle ka hal chahte hai to zara bataye k woh kya hai.

KUMAR: dekheye pehle to aap yeh baat samajye k Pakistan Kashmir ko kabhi azaad dekhna hi nhi chahta woh to bas Kashmir pe kabza karna chahta hai aur kuch nhi, Agar Pakistan Kashmir ko azaad dekhna chahta to chod deta ussi waqt jab UNITED NATIONS ne bola tha Army withdraw karne ko tab kiye hote to is waqt koi masla hi hota Kashmir azaad hota. yeh to pakistan tha jisne kashmir se army nikalne se mana kiya tha hum ne nhi.woh log Kashmir ko ya to Pakistan se milana chahte hai ya barbaad karna chahte hai.

Dekhye Pakistan India se haal hi main 71 ki jung haar chuka aur kabi India se jeet bhi nhi sakta yeh to aap bhi jante hai aur hum bi udar China bhi Kashmir ko itna hi chahta hai jitna Pakistan to le deke baat yeh k Kashmir akele survive nhi karsakta.

Ab main jo baat batane wala hu usko dyaan se suniye. Aaj nhi to kal aap Indian Army ke haath main aahi jayenge kuch dinu pehle hi aapki tanzeem ke kuch militants ko Indian Army ne maara aapki talash main poore gavu ko tehas nehas kardiya. Aaj nhi to kal aaptak bhi pohunch hi jayenge.

KUKA: to aap kya chahte hai ab hum surrender kare aapke saamne Ghulam bane, hamare baazu ne abhi haar nhi maani hai aur haan ek baat yaad rakhiye hame na appke Hindustan se kuch lena dena hai na Pakistan se humne yeh baat pehle hi saaf kardi hai hume bas Kashmir Azaad chahiye jo k JKLF ka Maqsad hai bas aur kuch nhi.

KUMAR: theek hai aap jo theek samje lekin main aapko ek baat bata du agar aapko lagta hai k Pakistan JKLF ka jo maqsad hai Kashmir ko Azaad karne usse khush hai aap bahut badi galat fahmi hai. Sach to yeh k Pakistan apko istemaal kar raha hai Kashmir main halat kharab karne ke liye taki aur Idian Army se ladne ke liye taki aakhir main woh apnee dusre tanzeemu ko beje Kashmir pe kabza karne ke liye.

KUKA: aisa bilkul nhi hai Pakistan hamari Azaadi wali tehreek se khush hai woh bas Kashmir ko Hindustan se alag dekhna chahta hai aur kuch nhi.

KUMAR: theek hai is waqt to main jaarha hu par parray sahab meri ek baat yaad rakhiyega aapki jo Pakistan ke baare main soch hai woh aapko ek din pashtawa karayegi. Aur woh din aap hame yaad karsakte hai kyunki hum aapke apne hai hamesha rahenge aap mane ya na mane.

Kumar leaves the place after the discussion and disappears like always.

DILAWAR who listened to everything carefully and now he and KUKA are alone in room.

DILAWAR: Parray mujhe lagta hai jo Kumar bola usmain kuch had tak sachaee to hai. kyunki Pakistan humko bina kisi maqsad ke support to nhi karege woh bhi itne hathyaar aur itna risk ke sath. Aur agar hamari Azaadi ki hi baat thi to JKLF ke bawajood HM (Hizbul Mujahideen) ko khada karne ki kya zarurat thi. HM ko to waise bhi Pakistan ka support hamse zyada hai to kahi ais na ho k kal HM hamare khilaaf hojaye aur humhi ko maarde.

KUKA: woh baat theek hai par Hindustan ka bhi barusa nhi kiya jasakta kab yeh log humko ko hi qurbaan kare kuch pata nhi hai.

DILAWAR: HM bhi deere deere hum logun se bagawat kar rha hai aur yahan se Hindustan ki Army encounter pe encounter karte jarhe hai. Ab hum yahan donu se kaise lade. Mujhe lagta hai ek waqt ayega jab hame donu main se kisi ko chunna padega ek taraf Hindustan hai Dusri taraf HM jiska seeda matlb Kashmir ko Pakistan main diya jaaye hamari azaadi hamare ilawa koi nhi chahta.

KUKA: theek hai sochte hai ispe dekhte hai kya hota hai, main kuch dinu keliye underground horha hu ,yahan Army ki movement bahut bad gayi hai.

DILAWAR: theek hai, acha Kumar phirse aaya to kya bolu.

KUKA : bolna ab koi mulaqat nhi hosakti hum apni jung lad rhe hai woh jaari rahegi.

DILAWAR: theek hai.

KUKA left.

Recently JKLF chief commander Ashfaq wani had been killed by Armed forces which was considered as the main architect of the armed struggle. A lot of Kashmiri youth were crossing the border to join the ranks of JKLF and HIZBUL MUJAHIDEEN. The different ideology between n two groups had also divided the Kashmir into two parts where JKLF presented to be secular and wants unification and independence of Kashmir, And HM wanted to merge Kashmir to Pakistan. Now more people joining the both groups was also rising of the conflict not only with India but between the Kashmiris too.

JKLF was getting week day by day Yasin Malik had been now in jail from last three years most of the commanders were dead now only one commander was left whose search was going day and night by Indian army village to village house to house not a single corner was left unsearched. A crackdown was put in KUKA's village Hajan which is still considered as biggest crackdown ever. Army was searching for KUKA and his associates,

In between a man who was believed to be the closest to Kuka was **Ashiq Lateef** (a great drama performer and poet) he was so skilled man that he put on the women's costume and roamed freely among military personals in village for days of crackdown but later he was captured by army.

After days of search KUKA was not traced anywhere army lifted the cracked from Hajan.

Here HM managed to create dominance and growing enmity for JKLF put KUKA in thought about what KUMAR earlier mentioned.

Days passed, everywhere the only thing you could hear was silence and fear In Hajan and in whole Kashmir. HM increased gathering and recruitments in villages which itself was putting a pressure on JKLF about their beliefs and goals.

After some days All Parties Hurriyat Conference was formed. A group of Kashmiri politicians its goal is Kashmir's right to self-determination and kept the question of independence or merger with Pakistan open. Where armed movement continues in Kashmir against JKLF those were the only group now who wanted Kashmir to be completely independent from India as well as Pakistan.

According to Article posted In Adi Magazine Indian Paramilitary Border Security Force (BSF) massacres more than 100 unarmed civilians and burns down several neighbourhoods. In April, a prominent Kashmiri heart surgeon and JKLF sympathizer, Abdul Ahad Guru, is shot dead. (Later a key Indian bureaucrat in Kashmir, Wajahat Habibullah, will blame Indian security agencies to have conspired with an HM activist to kill Guru.) In October, BSF kills 55 Kashmiris who had assembled after Friday prayers in Bijbehara town in South Kashmir. Despite several accords, intergroup rivalry leads to frequent clashes between the JKLF and the HM. Better trained HM cadres kill dozens of JKLF members.

These all events were creating more mess and nothing seems to make sense because in Kashmir every party and militant groups were divided by ideology and power.

Then comes the time when Kashmiri's were getting killed not only from armed forces but from all militant groups from all parties and armed forces during the encounters and protests.

JKLF chief Yasin Malik was in prison since 1990 and now it had become more difficult to maintain the group on tact and to discuss about future steps and objectives.

Kumar was also waiting for the correct time and frame to encounter with KUKA so that he could pull out some solution to the situation.

A month has passed KUKA was not seen in his village his over ground associates were also underground in fear that army would take them to torture for KUKA's whereabouts.

Finally, the day came Kumar managed to send message to KUKA for meeting which he agreed and a meeting was scheduled at Parray's house.

Next day evening KUMAR, KUKA, DILAWAR and all his close men gathered.

KUMAR: Kaise hai Parray sahab

KUKA: aapki dua se zinda hai abhi, baaki hum logu ko doondke marne main apke mulk ne koi kasar to chodi nhi hai

KUMAR: jinaab kaisi baate kar rhe hai aap, yeh mulk apka bhi to hai.

Haa bas aap thoda sa naraaz hogaye hai humse baaki hum Kashmir ko apna taaj kal bhi samjte the aur aaj bhi samjte hai.

Baaki rahi aapki baat aap hamare dost hai, humne bhi dosti nibane main koi kasar chodi ho to bataye.

KUKA: Kumar sahab ab aap seede mudde pe aayeye k ab jo halaat Kashmir main huve hai usmain aap hamari kya madad karsakte hai.

Kuch karsakte bhi ya nhi.

KUMAR: Kar hum bahut kuch sakte hai Kashmir ke liye bhi aur aapke liye bhi bas aapka saath chahiye usmain.

KUKA: meri madad woh kaise.

KUMAR: itna to aap samajte hai k jo apki tanzeem jo Kashmir ki azaadi ke liye uthi thi ab uss halat main hain nhi k kuch karsakte hai kyunki ab baaki tanzeemain bhi khadi huvi hai jo mujhe lagta hai aapke iraade se kuch khaas itifaq nhi rakhte. Unke liye bas Pakistan hi sab kuch hai woh Kashmir ko Pakistan se milane ke liye kuch bhi karsakte hai balki kashmiriyu ko bhi maar rhe hai.

Iska matlb yeh hai k jis Pakistan ke baruse pe aapne Hindustan se bagawat karne ka faisla liya tha woh Pakistan ab HM (HIZBUL MUJAHIDEEN) main zyada se zyada logu ko shaamil kar rhe hai jo k aapke liye bhi utna hi khatra hai jitna hamare liye.

KUKA: Kumar sahab aap hame Kashmir ki halat se waqif na karaye hame sab khabar hai.

DILAWAR who was also present in room.

DILAWAR: KUKA mujhe lagta hai KUMAR sahab sahi bol rhe hai Pakistan ne dhoka kiya hai hamare saath pehle bola k Kashmir ko azaad dekhna chahte hai aur JKLF ko support kiya ab Kashmir ko HIZBUL MUJAHIDEEN ka gadd banana chahte hai.

KUMAR: bilkul yehi baat main kabse samja rha hu k Pakistan kisi ka saga nhi hai woh bas peet peche war karna janta hai aur kuch nhi aur unko kashmiriyu se utni bhi khas hamdardi nhi hai jitni dikhate hai.

KUKA: Kumar sahab aapne kuch madad karne ki baat ki thi shayid zara uske baare kuch bolea. Hum samjte hai kiske kya iraade hai aur kon kya chahta hai.

KUMAR: ji yehi main apko samjane ki koshish kar rha tha shukur hai aap yeh baat to samjgaye.

Ab suniye main kya keh raha hu,

Pakistan ne aap loguke zariye ab apni tanzeemu ko Kashmir main khada kar diya hai jo ab Kashmir main har jagah tabahi machadenge. Ab aapko faisla karna hai k aap kya dekhna chahte hai. Main itna keh sakta hu k Kashmir ko Pakistan nhi sambal sakta kyunki uske baad china se bhi ladna padega. Ab raha apke pass ek hi raasta woh hai Hindustan ke saath rehne ka, hum aapko suraksha bhi de sakte hai donu mulku se aur aapko to hamne kabhi apne se alag to smja nhi hai.

KUKA: theek hai Kumar sahab hum apki baat se sehmat hai bataye aage kya karna hai.

KUMAR: aapko hamare saath aana padega uske liye, agar aap chahte hai k iss masle ka koi hal nikle.

KUKA: aapke saath, Matlab surrender karke jail jaavu ya kisi militant ke haathu maara javu aisa keh rahe aap.

KUMAR: nhi aisa bilkul nhi hoga maine aisa kab bola.

KUKA: to phir aapke kehne ka kya matlb tha.

KUMAR: mere kehne ka matlab yeh hai k aap Surrender kardo apne saathiyu ke saath baaki main sambal lunga.

KUKA: aap kaisi baatein kar rhe Surrender aur main, woh bhi apne saathiyu ke saath, hargiz nhi aisa kabhi nhi hoga.

KUMAR: arey main aapko surrender karke jail nhi bej rha hu bas surrender karne ko bol rha hu baaki rahi uske baad ki baat uske liye mere pass plan hai. Agar aap surrender nhi bhi karte to aaj nhi to kal aap Army ya HM ke hatthu mare jayenge.

KUKA: acha theek hai maan liya maine karliya suurender uske baad kya.

KUMAR: aap surrender kariye to sahi main aapko isse zyada powers dunga aur kisi se chupne ki zarurat bhi nhi padegi.

KUKA: woh kaise.

DILAWAR: parray agar Kumar sahab bol rhe hai to unke pass kuch to plan hogana. Mujhe lagta hai Kumar sahab sahi keh rhe hai.

KUKA: par Dilawar tu baat nhi samaj rha hai. Kashmir main har jagah HM ne kabza karliya hai hum Surrender karenge to HM poora Kashmir leke Pakistan ke haath main dedega aur uska matlb samajta hai, uska matlb hum sab ki moat.

KUMAR: aisa kuch nhi hoga, balki main jo keh raha hu waisa karo baaki mujhpe barusa karo main sab sambhalunga.

KUKA: nhi Kumar sahab ab hame kisi pe barusa nhi hai Pakistan ne dhoka kiya Hindustan pe to waise bhi barusa nhi hai hume.

KUMAR: theek hai phir suno. Agar tum Kashmir aur khud ko theek dekhna chahte ho to tum apne loguke saath surrender kardo. Baaki rahi HM walu ki baat unko Army dekhlegi aur hame usmain aapki madad chahiye kyunki unke chipe huva jagahu ke baare main aap logu se behtar koi nhi jaanta. Aur pehle hum in Pakistani HM walun ko yahan se nikale main aapse waada karta hu k aap pe koi case nhi hoga uske baad yahan election karana hai usmain aap apni party khadi karlo uska support main khud karunga.

Aur mere support ka matlb samjte hai aap.

DILAWAR: parray maine bola tha k Kumar sahab ke pass kuch to plan hoga.

KUKA: theek main aapke saath hu main apne aadmiyu ke saath mashwara karke aapko bolta hu kahan hoga surrender.

KUMAR: aap waise karo jaise maine bola baaki mujpe chod do.

KUKA: acha mujhe is waqt nikalna hoga yahan se zyada waqt nhi rehsakta.

KUMAR: theek hai main aapko surrender ki jagah ka patah bolta hu, mujhe kuch din do mujhe upar apne seniors se baat karni padegi kyunki ab Kashmir main bahut kuch badalne wala hai hamesha ke liye.

DILAWAR: theek hai Kumar sahab aapko jab bhi milna hoga aap mere pass direct aajayega.

KUMAR: theek hai chalta hu is waqt.

everyone left immediately one after another.

Days after the meeting KUKA surrendered with other 28 close men before Indian army.

Here in parliament of India, a resolution was passed which claimed Kashmir to be integral part of India and non-negotiable therefore. As a word given to Kuka, he was not arrested nor were any of his men.

And now the history of Kashmir was going to change forever.

More forces were sent to Kashmir as an estimate it was now half million Indian soldiers in Kashmir, they were sent to conduct elections and to tackle with militancy which was not an easy task to do.

But KUMAR as always had plan for that too. He let KUKA and his men to keep the weapons the group of KUKA which was linked with JKLF was called Ikhwan ul Muslimeen, And now KUKA formed new group which was called as "Ikhwan ul Muslimoon" with some other small groups like MM (Muslim Mujahideen).

From south Kashmir Liaqat ali khan also joined hands with the group of KUKA PARRAY.

now this group had given task to help Army to clear all militancy in Kashmir, And conduct elections.

Ikhwanis and MM kill dozens of Jamaat Islami members in the countryside, forcing many to run away to Srinagar. An HM vs Ikhwan/MM fight ensues, leading to intense bloodshed. HM loses ground due to persistent Ikhwani/MM assaults.

This was the time when counter insurgency started in whole Kashmir which sparked many dread full events.

KUKA formed the group and different responsibilities were given to people like Dilawar was kept as to maintain finance and other his associates were given areas to handle and a core motive was discussed in different meetings. And the aim to make Kashmir free from militancy was planned. Many civilian basically the earlier supporters of KUKA PARRAY joined the hands with the outfit and picked up arms to go for fight with militancy. Recruitments were continued and more and more people showed interest in the group wich made this group the largest group till now.

Among this new group there were some of the names which can never be forgotten by Kashmir especially these people where the main faces of the insurgency and the group which was now famous with name IKHWAN in whole Kashmir.

- The leader Mohammad Yousuf Parray aka **KUKA PARRAY**
- Second name after KUKA is Ghulam Rasool Parray aka **KAAKH** (Kuka's elder brother)
- Commander Ab Rashid Parray aka **RASHID BILLA**
- Commander Fayaz Mir aka **FAYAZ NAWBADI**
- Commander Manzoor Ahmad parray aka **WAFADAR** (Kuka's nephew)
- The finance minister Abdul Rehman Parray aka **DILAWAR**

Some ikhwani militants posing for the camera

Chapter 3

Rashid Billa

Now it was clear that Kashmir was divided into two parts from one side Ikhwani's was taking ground and eliminating militants other side militants was fighing with both Army and Ikhwan. Meanwhile Army had chosen to be aside and enjoyed the fight between two Kashmiri groups which was fulfilling their goal too.

One of the commanders among the group was Ab Rashid Parray alias Rashid billa. Going back to billa's life he was a distant relative of KUKA PARRAY.

after his father's death, Billa, a labourer, was appointed as Plantation Watcher in Hajan zone. But Billa never joined his duty as Parray wanted to use him for something big. Though Billa was one of the Ikhwani's who had not taken any proper arms and ammunition training, but proved to be most dreaded one with the weapons.

Young Rashid Billa holding his AK47 riffle

Hizbul mujahideen was trying to recruit more and more people, brain wash them so they can pick up the weapons and fight against Army and now Ikhwan's also. But Ikhwan proved to be one step ahead of them always they would go to door to door to warn people that if they are found in links in militants they would be killed without any mercy.

Ikhwani's reached out to militants operating in the enforcing villages to join them. Those who refused were either killed or "banished". they kidnapped their fathers, brothers, even mothers and sisters to pressurize militants to surrender and join them.

The differences between the ideology of Ikwani's and militants had crossed the limit now where militants were pro Pakistani's, and ikhwani's were now a part of Indian forces every other day a militant would be killed by ikhwani's and in return militants would kill one of the ikhwani's. The bloodshed seemed to be not stopping any sooner. Both the groups started enlarging their groups by adjoining more and more people and weapon backups day by day.

Rashid Billa joined the group now and was made a commander after four months of joining. He was given Hajan town to look on and all other areas were divided accordingly among commanders by the supreme commander KUKA PARRAY.

not all needed coercion to join Kuka Parray, some of them came voluntarily as they saw an opportunity in new **Ikhwan**. Within days, he created a dreaded force with 'commanders' in almost every surrounding village.

Most important member was Abdul Rehman Parray aka **Dilawar**, group's "finance minister". He had played an important role in joining hands with Indian forces.

Once the group was complete, militant listing started in Bandipora. Billa was assigned to collect data of rich and affluent. Once this process was complete, Kuka Parray decided to formally announce his association with the army.

Before ikhwan's surrender **1993,** Ghulam Qadir Dar, then 44, a contractor and truck-driver from Saderkot Bala, was stopped by half-a-dozen militants outside Hajan.

After parking Dar's truck near the bridge, militants belonging to Parray's Ikhwan-ul-Muslimeen, took him along. By midnight Dar was shuttled between five hideouts to ensure he remembers nothing.

Finally, as it started getting dark, Dar was handed over to Billa. Dar was accused of working with the army and passing on information about the militant movement.

They let him go after his family paid 60000rs.

Once he reached home, He wanted to forget the episode and move on, but it didn't happen. He was asked to visit Parray's elder brother after one week.

When Dar presented himself before Ghulam Ahmad Parray, he was told that his alleged links with the army has irked rank and file of Mujahideen. "Then as a way out, he offered me a position as Ikhwan's commander," said Dar. "Also, he promised to put 20 gunmen under my command."

Dar refused politely. But his refusal didn't go down well with Parray so That day onwards, whenever Parry's men visited Saderkot Bala to collect 'funds' for militants, Dar's house would get a special knock. He was always asked to pay ten times more than the rest of the villagers, recalls Dar. "I would pay without question, knowing they can kill anybody at will."

While Kuka Parray became Supreme Commander, Rashid Billa took care of Hajan as the base Commander. Billa appointed his deputies almost in all surrounding villages.

This group helped Kuka Parray control entire Bandipora district, They all reported to Billa, who in turn reported to Kuka Parray.

There was many more men who were famous in those days and who was very close associate to KUKA like,

- From Bandipore it was USMAN MAJID he himself boasted about killing hundreds, he is still a political activist and now living a very responsible citizens life under the protection of the state and escapes the prosecution.

- Commander **Rashid Khan** who was given the area of Kupwara. He was one of the dreaded one who misused the power given by KUKA to fight against militants, instead he murdered a lot of civilians. There are nine murder cases registered against him, but he has never been called to court. He murdered many more civilians whom there is no record. Rashid khan was also making money from extortion. He lives a secure, respectable life in Kupwara and runs a successful business as construction contractor.

- Momma Kanna was a junior employee in the forest department earning a meagre Rs300 a month before he joinined hands with Ikhwan, as I earlier mentioned a lot of people saw an opportunity to earn so they jumped into it. His name was synonymous with extortion, rape, torture, and extra judicial killings across the valley in the 90's. He admits a direct hand in neutralizing over 5000 rebels which is not true as such but he was involved in lots of killings. He was awarded a padma shri in 2010. His Magam residence is guarded by a company of 100 personnel of the paramilitary CRPF.

- Ghulam Mohammad lone aka **Papa Kishtwari** worked as a watchman before joining hands with Ikhwan and going on killing spree. He is responsible for killing of hundreds. He is currently in Central Jail in Srinagar.

Apart from Billa, Ikhwan's inner group had Nazir aka Captain; Manzoor Parray aka **Wafadaar** (Kuka Parry's nephew) and Ghulam Rasool Parray aka **Kaakh** (Kuka Parray's elder brother).

Now Ikhwani's divided into small groups were operating from Baramulla to Bandipora to Kupwara where most militants were active.

One day they picked up two al Jihad militants and killed them in cold blood in Hajan town in broad daylight, One of them was Abdul Rashid aka Shera.

After that killing, Kuka Parray started executing his plans based on the lists prepared by his 'commanders'.

Billa was entrusted to implement the first phase. That evening, Rashid Billa led party barged into Abdul Khaliq's house in Madwan village and dragged him out. He was head of a *Jamat-e-Islami* run school in Hajan. They took him to nearby Preng village and shot him dead.

A few days later 'commander' Bashir Yar entered another Jamati's house in Ajas village and killed Ghulam Ahmad Rather.

To keep the fear alive in the hearts of locals, a youngster named Mohammad Yousuf Peer, was dragged through the Hajan streets in broad daylight and then killed. He was from nearby Paribal village. "Nobody could move a muscle when they shot him in full public view. Peer was accused of working as Hizb-ul-Mujahideen's over ground worker.

These back-to-back killings unnerved almost every militant outfit active in the area. To send a message, one evening, posters of Hizb-ul-Mujahideen appeared in Hajan town warning Ikhwan men of dire consequences. It sent shivers among the locals as everybody feared how Kuka Parray and his gang will react.

The next day, at around noon, Billa paraded four young men from nearby villages through Hajan town.

They were tied with a rope, which was held by an Ikhwan, who dragged them all the way to Billa's camp. While three of them were let go after their families paid the ransom, the fourth one, Mohammad Ashraf Parray, 26, was tortured and killed. "They took him (Ashraf) to a carpet weaver's house and pressed him inside the loom till his bones crushed.

While nobody dared to criticize Kuka Parray and his men even in their private conversations, there was a labourer named Majid who confronted Billa once. "I still shiver when I remember that day," said Majid.

After the first round of Hizb posters failed to have any impact, another set appeared in Hajan. This time the tone was much straight and warnings more clear: give up bloodshed or face consequences.

The same day four local boys visited Gulmarg for a night of peace and recreation. "One of them was my younger brother," recalls Majid.

Next day when the boys returned to Hajan, they were picked up by Billa and his men. "They tortured him like animals. They showed a matchstick after sprinkling petrol on his back," recalls Majid.

When Majid learned about his brother's 'arrest' he ran straight to Billa's camp and dared him to come out. "I was not thinking straight then," said Majid. "I was acting purely out of anger."

The same evening his brother was sent home with a warning for Majid. "Tell your brother we will come for him soon," they told my brother.

Next evening Billa came to his house with his men as promised. "They said nothing and started firing at my house," recalls Majid. "It was sheer luck that nobody got hurt."

After firing around two hundred rounds they left, but with one more warning: we will be back again. "Three days later he came back and took my brother along," said Majid. "It cost me Rs 15000 and number of middlemen to get him out safely."

The ransom money was used to sustain and feed the growing Ikhwan's appetite. But there were other means of income too. "Kuka Parray's finance minister **DILAWAR** was a very smart man," said Khan. "He knew how to arrange money."

It was Dilawar's advice that Kuka Parray told his masters that in order to clear the militancy from the region we have to work on this plan.

The plan was to cut down the adjoining jungle, government nursery in Hajan and a huge plantation, to flush out the hiding militants. "He got the entire jungle cleared within a few days," said Khan. "The actual plan was to sell the willow (a tree which is used to make cricket bats), timber which he did. It helped him raise crores."

Once the financial issues were taken care of by **DILAWAR**, the group now wanted to enjoy their lives! "For them, the enjoyment always came at helpless people's expenses," said Khan.

Within a few days the incidents of eve-teasing, molestation and forceful marriages by Kuka Parray's men peaked.

It all started after an Ikhwan cornered two young girls when they had gone to wash utensils at a stream. "One of the girls probably pushed him away when he tried to touch her inappropriately," said Khan.

He fled from the spot when a few women raised an alarm, but with a warning. The same evening the Ikhwani's barged into the girl's house with his men and dragged her out.

"He beat everybody in the house," recalls Khan. "People could hear her helpless cries all night long. Only Allah knows what he did with that girl."

A few days later, one of the Billa's bodyguards abducted a bride. The same evening, she was forcefully married to her kidnapper. Next morning, Ikhwani's abducted her real husband and tortured him. "He was released after his family paid a ransom of Rs 40,000," said Khan. Nobody knows what happened to that boy, some say he committed suicide.

By the end of 1995, Kuka Parray's stature and patronage grew manifolds and he floated his own political party: Jammu Kashmir Awami League (JKAL). He appointed himself as party's chairman and began preparing for upcoming 1996 assembly elections.

When the election came, nobody except National Conference's Mohammad Akbar Lone, dared to contest against Parray.

"Those were difficult times for everyone living in the area," recalls Akbar Lone, now a third-time lawmaker from Naidkhai Sonawari. Lone recalls how he used to travel stealthily through Sumbal, to avoid confrontation with Parray's men. They could have killed anyone at will. said Lone.

Often, locals used to visit Lone in Srinagar, where he was stationed, with complaints that Parray's men had taken their vehicles on gun-point, or looted money from them. "It was a routine. I could only request police to intervene, beyond that I too was helpless," said Lone,

Days before polling, in a group of threes and fours, Ikhwani's visited all villages in Sonawari belt to seek votes for Parray. One such party, led by Billa was sent to Saderkot Balla and its adjoining villages. "They visited every single house telling people: vote for Kuka Parray or face the music," recalls Khan. "Even NC's cadre didn't dare to oppose his edict."

But there was one man who not only dared to talk against Kuka Parray and his men, but voted for his opponent. It was Ghulam Qadir Dar, the same truck driver whom Billa had kidnapped earlier. Dar's daredevil act enraged rank and file of Ikhwan, who saw it as rebellion!

October 5, 1996, election results were announced and Kuka Parray was declared a winner from Sonawari constituency. Same evening Billa and his men came to Saderkot Bala village looking for Dar.

"I was listening to the radio when I heard one of the Ikhwani's calling my name," recalls Dar. "He was asking me to come out."

But Dar's family didn't allow him to go out; instead, his son forced him to go upstairs. There were around 30 men in our courtyard. They had taken a position with their weapons pointed towards our front door,

When Billa and his men started firing in air Dar's wife Hajra, 37, ran out to reason with them. "As she reached near the door, they fired at her and she fell down instantly," said Dar, as if reliving the dreadful scene. Next, Hajra's daughter Jawa, 18, ran to pick her mother, and she too was shot. Then they shot dead Dar's elder son Abdul Salam Dar, 21, who went out to help his mother and sister. "Finally they killed my brother's son Abdul Rashid Dar," said Dar. "He was inside the corridor. He was just 22."

Shocked, Dar couldn't react as he watched four of his family members being killed in a span of two minutes. "He (Rashid Billa) wiped out my entire family in front of my eyes and I could do nothing."

After Billa and his men left they went to another house in the locality and shot dead Saifudin Dar, 45. "They didn't stop there," recalls Dar. Within half-an-hour, Billa killed Ghulam Rasool Dar, 35, and Ghulam Nabi Dar, 32, too. "That night was like doomsday for Saderkot Bala village," said Khan.

Later Dar identified seven of the 30 men including Billa, who killed his family.

The killings in Saderkot Bala unveiled the monster who was hidden in Billa.

Within next 15 days militants killed five of Parray's close aides in a mine blast in Hajan.

The bloodshed on the roads of Hajan and its adjoining areas was on its peak, If you are a normal civilian you had no choice left other than witnessing the bloodshed and remain silent if you want to see yourself alive.

Here Kuka wasn't happy with the bloodshed Billa had done in aggression, Billa came back to Hajan where celebration was still on.

BILLA: Parray uske poore khandan ko khatam karke aaya hu, hamare khilaaf bahut bol rha tha, ab uski aane wali nasal tak yaad rakhegi k hamare khillaf hone ka kya anjaam hota hai.

KUKA: Billa tumhara gussa jayaz hai par itna mat mat kar k poori party ko nuksaan hojaye. Hum waise bhi jeet gaye hai election yeh sab karne ki kya zarurat thi.

BILLA: par parray woh hamare khilaaf bahut bol rha tha ulta sab ko NC(National Conference) ko vote daalne ko bol rha tha main usko kaise choddta.

KUKA: lekin Billa koi hamare khillaf hai to zaroori nahi hai k jaake poore khandaan ko maar dalke aavo aapne gusse ko qaabu main rakh nhi to baakhuda main ek din tumhe khud goli mardunga, samja.

BILLA: theek hai samaj gaya aage se dyaan rakhunga.

KUKA: chal abhi ja thoda khana wana kha le rogan josh banaya hai tere liye jaa apne saathiyu ko bhi khila.

BILLA: theek hai jaata hu, gussa to nhi hai hona merese.

KUKA: jaa abhi khana kha chup chap bade natak karta hai ajkal tu.

BILLA: theek hai theek hai jata hu, dara rha mereko.

Billa went to the room and started having **dinner with his men.** While other Ikhwani men were all present in house and enjoyed the win of the assembly elections.

Where Ikhwan was in its peak so was HM(Hizbul Mujahideen) also in its peak, for some time it was being very difficult to decide for the people to decide that is even anyone of the outfit really working for the welfare of the civilians because the HM(Hizbul Mujahideen) who claimed to be fighting for the people of Kashmir were killing people for silly reasons like personal enmity, land disputes, for women and many more reasons that could not be justified as it is in the favour of Kashmiri people. That was one of the reasons that people had given some sort of support to Ikhwan,

The fight between Ikhwan and HM had made whole Kashmir some sort of battle field where every other day you could see the corpse on the roads, after some time HM made their ideology clear in Kashmir that they want Kashmir to be merged with Pakistan.

After some days of the election BILLA got the info of some of the HM militants who were hiding in one of the locals house, Billa immediately took some of his men with him and left for the encounter. Meanwhile Indian Army had left Ikhwan in battle field as they were succeed in various operations because of their knowledge about the their strategies and local information.

BILLA reached to the place where militants were hiding out and cordoned off the house with his men and shouted.

BILLA: abe kahan chupe ho darr ke. Agar nhi darre ho to to ab darr ka pata chalega kyunki Billa aaya hai aaj khud.

One of BILLA's men shouted: Billa lagta hai darr ke maare gala sookh gaya hai awaaz nhi nikal rhi hai.

BILLA fired some shots in air with AK47

BILLA: Qamar (one of the Pakistani HM militant famous in the area) mujhe pata hai tum hi ho, tumhe kya lagta hai tu yahan jaan dega apni, aur udar Salah ud din bhooka Rahega tere liye, aansu bahayega tere liye, arey aaj raat hi tere naam ki biryani khayega, aur tujhe lagta hai tu Kashmir ko Pakistan se milayega, galat bilkul galat. Waise baat to ek sahi hai k milavunga to tujhe main zaroor yahan isi waqt isi mitti main, chal tu bhi kya yaad rakhega ki Kashmir ki miti main qabar naseeb huvi.

Billa and his men started firing at the house continuously for half n hour where two of the militants in which Qamar was one among were killed.

There was so much fear in people even nobody could attend or arrange the funeral and last prayer (Jinaza) for the HM militants. Everyone knew the consequences if they would come out in favour of HM militants in anyways. Army would take the bodies and bury them in the graveyards.

Chapter 4

Fayaz Nawbadi

Where Billa was very famous and got immense success to create fear and the hold on the areas which were given to him. No one in the area among kids and aged who wouldn't know Billa and his stories were getting famous among the people who would give example of Billa as a monster whenever they were telling stories to kids.

PARRAY was focusing on main game and handling officers and other players in ground had left an army of monsters in Kashmir publicly and one among the commanders who had been given the areas of Sumbal, Srinagar and Ganderbal that was none other than "Nawbadi" Fayaz Nawbadi himself. A merciless and fearless man who would do anything to fulfil his ego, who would kill anyone at his will.

Fayaz Ahmad Mir aka Fayaz Nawbadi stayed mostly in Srinagar and adjoining areas. He would often pick anyone for money.

During the fall of JKLF, Fayaz Nawbadi an arm trained man was in jail. The enmity between JKLF and HM had crossed all the limits. There is a village in sonawari called Nawabadi Mohalla.

Nawabadi Mohalla may pass off as just another small village in the Sonawari, but for its street lights that make it stand apart. Those familiar with the village, don't dare to take it for any other village, anyways.

Nawabadi has entered Kashmir's lexicon as a word that strikes terror. There were many villages in Kashmir that became hotbeds of counterinsurgency but Nawabadi was one name that stuck.

A village of some three hundred people, two and a half kilometres from Safapora.

In picture Fayaz Ahmad Mir aka Fayaz Nawbadi

A few kilomteres from father of counterinsurgency Kuka Parrey's Hajan village, Nawabadi Mohalla gave Ikhwan some of its most dreaded men. Many remember the village as the birthplace of ruthless renegades, like Fayaz Mir alias Fayaz Nawabadi, notorious for extortion, rape, politically motivated killings. For the state security apparatus, that patronised them, these men were important to break the back of militancy in the Sonawari-Ganderbal belt and by extension whole of Kashmir. So they did. Hardly anyone was spared.

Perhaps because many of the first renegades came from Nawabadi village, the name in local parlance became a synonym for all the counterinsurgents or police informers. An alternative name for Ikhwan, the largest renegade group.

After the switching of Ikhwan to counter insurgency, apart from the ruthless renegades who emerged from Nawabadi Mohalla, the village provided a haven for all counter-insurgents. Even though only a few from the village carried out the dirty work, almost all residents were Ikhwan sympathisers.

Nawabdis trace their shift of allegiance to the killing of a JKLF militant from the village by Hizbul Mujahideen in inter faction rivalry in 1993.

Manzoor Ahmad was the first postgraduate from the village. He did his MA in Urdu from Kashmir University. Later he joined Jammu Kashmir Students Liberation Front and crossed the LoC for arms training. After this he joined Jammu Kashmir Liberation Front as Deputy District Commander. This was around the time when animosities between Hizbul Mujahideen (HM) and JKLF were building up.

While on his way back from Sopore Manzoor was picked up by Hizbul Mujahideen. "They accused him of being an

Indian agent," say the residents, "but at that time it was widely known that Manzoor was a man of character. It was actually that Ahsan Dar wanted him to join HM."

When news of Manzoor's abduction spread in the area, desperate attempts started to secure his release. "The negotiations were carried out at the highest level; almost all the known militants and separatist leaders were involved.

The residents were promised his release. "But he was not released. We kept on searching for him. We formed search parties and would search for him throughout the area," says Kawaam Din. But the search yielded no result. At this time Fayaz, Manzoor's cousin was in jail.

"Even Syed Ali Shah Geelani searched for him in his car. He told us that he had spent 13000 rupees searching for him," he says, "Moulvi Abbas Ansari and Saleem Geelani also mediated but to no avail."

Demands for Manzoor's release were building up. People were protesting. The Hajan bazaar remained shut down for 25 days at a stretch.

Then, residents say, a HM rebel Shams-u-Din informed the villagers that Manzoor had been killed on the second day of his abduction, and lay buried in Hari-Taar, on the banks of Jehlum near Sopore.

"We rushed to the spot. Some militants from HM were guarding the spot, and they fired on the crowd. People from the surrounding areas like Shah-Gund joined in and we retrieved the body," adds Kawaam. The eruption of emotions and sentiments was spontaneous. "It was an angry crowd, which sees nothing in rage. On the way from Hari-Taar to Nawabadi Mohalla, around 14 houses belonging to Jamat-e-Islami (JeI) members or sympathisers were set ablaze," adds Kamaal. "It was a day which this region cannot forget. It was a day of pain."

After this the rift between JKLF and HM-JeI deepened. A civil war sort of situation ensued where people from both sides were being assassinated. The Nawabadis became fiercely anti-HM and anti-Jamaat. "In all this all the militant organisations united against HM, and opened a united front against them," he says.

Peer Ziya-ud-Din of Asham, a JKLF sympathiser and father of Nazir Ahmad Geelani of JKLF was also gunned down by HM. This added oil to the fire. Around 500-600 people would die in this infighting, many among them were civilians.

Fayaz, now released, joined the Ikhwan, and with the wounds of Manzoor's loss still fresh, many Nawabadis followed him into the fold. "When we had seen the body of Manzoor, we could see nothing else. He had come out for the cause. We had followed in his footsteps, but Jamaat and Hizbul mujahideen ruined it. They targeted everyone who was not their supporter. We could tolerate it no further," says an ex-counter insurgent.

Fayaz was merciless. He soon gained notoriety and was gifted the post of commander-in-chief of the Ikhwan. Kuka Parray reigned as the supremo. Thus started the reign of terror. After that it was "catch and kill," accepts Kawaam.

Though the actual gun wielding Nawabdis did not number more than 10, all the counter insurgents in Valley – estimated to be between 1,000-1,200- came to be known by the name.

The shifting allegiances of Nawabadis created animosities with adjoining villages. Residents recall that after Manzoor's death the adjoining villages in Safapora and Bandipora enforced a boycott of the village.

"The shopkeepers won't provide us amenities. They were not given medicines even for around six months," says a Nawabadi resident.

Mohammad Sidiq, father of Fayaz Nawabadi says the boycott forced them to loot any trucks that passed the village. "But we would pay them," he said in the same breath.

In coming years, the response from the Nawabadis was often brutal. Fayaz Nawabadi walked the streets like a king.

"Even policemen had to look down while walking past him," says a resident of Ganderbal.

He was the most notorious export of Nawabadi Mohalla to the rest of Kashmir. The Commander-in-Chief of Kuka Parray's Ikhwan, he is said to have killed hundreds of people. "If his eyes fell on something he liked, it had to be his," the resident adds. One day his eyes fell on a new scooter parked in the Safapora market. The scooter belonged to Waseem, a 21 year old.

"Waseem would not just let go of his new scooter when the Nawabadis asked him to give it to them,". Fayaz then walked up to him, and held him by his throat. He then pumped bullets into him. Waseem fell to ground. When a shopkeeper raised his voice, he too met the same fate. One more onlooker also fell to the ground. "Three innocent people died that day. With three dead bodies on the streets Fayaz issued his threat, "People of Safapora, whoever goes against us will meet a similar fate," he says.

Fayaz would be accompanied by his trusted lieutenants, Abdul Hamid Mir alias Nikka Bhai, Mohammad Afzal Mir alias Commander Adil, Ghulam Nabi Mir alias Kaka among others, all Nawabadis. They reign of terror engulfed Sonawari, Safapora, Ganderbal areas. Hardly anyone was spared, but the families of militants and Jamat-e-Islami supporters were especially targeted. It started a wave of migration from the area to the urban areas. Many people even left the state. "No one was safe," says the resident. The killings continued. Saif-u-Din Bhat, a 60-years-old teacher from Safapora was killed because his brother was associated with HM. Another teacher Abdul Karim Bhat was killed because of links with Jamat-e-Islami. A bank employee, Mohammad Afzal of Yongoora Chak also fell to bullets, for unknown reasons. The number is estimated to be above 300. Some locals say the number of the people killed was much higher than 300.

Nawabadis once went to the house of a Jamaat-e-Islami sympathiser in Banyari village. The man was not there. "The routine would have been to harass the family and leave," says Yasir, a resident of the area. But on this day death was in the air. "One of the Nawabadi commanders caught hold of a six month old son of the man," he says. Then hell broke loose. "He flung the child into the air, and the Nawabadi party started firing." The infant came down in smithereens.

Tales of the atrocities abound. "One more case still resonates in the minds and hearts of people. There was a girl in Asham, a beautiful girl, Nazima, the daughter of one Ghulam Mohammad Lone. And then their eyes fell on her,

Nazima was kidnapped and raped. "For days together no one knew of her, Then details related to her emerged. It was Fayaz actually who had sought her. When she had resisted she was raped, by many Nawabadis, They raped her for days. She became pregnant. After a few months she was let go. In the meantime, Ashraf Nawabidi, Fayaz's brother started pursuing Nazima's sister. She too was kidnapped.

The family decided to protest against it and hit the road with some of the neighbours.

And some slogans and some tears were going together side by side.

-Naarayee takbeer

Allah u Akbar

-Fayaz Nawbadi

Murdabad Murdabad

-Zoor Zoor se awaz do

Insaaf do Insaaf do

But there was no one to listen the outcry of these people. They expected justice but the family would not have protested if they would have known what was to come next, The Nawabadis converged on the Asham market. Nazima was dragged out on the street. Fayaz oversaw everything. "What transpired next is engraved in the psyche of the people there forever,

The eight month pregnant woman was held forcibly. Then her clothes were torn. After this she was paraded naked. "Fayaz pulled the trigger, and shot her in the abdomen first. He kept on shooting and shouting –

Fayaz Nawbadi: Anjaam dekhliye hamare khilaaf jane ka Fayaz Nawbadi ke khilaaf jane ka,

Agar kisi aur ko humse koi bhi problem hai to aajavo usse bhi sula dete hai. Dyaan se suno tum logu ko Fayaz Nawbadi se koi nhi bacha sakta, agar zinda rehna chahte ho to chup chap raho kisi ki awaaz na aaye. Aur agar in logu ki tarah hamare khilaaf javoge to yehi anjaam hoga tum logu ka bhi.

Nazima died on the spot. Her sister is still with Ashraf.

Even after an incident of this sort, no one raised a voice. That was the peak of Nawabadi terror.

The biggest gang war on peak in the history of Kashmir, ikhwanis were searching for militants door to door and would shoot the at sight in return HM militants would kill ikhwani when they would get chance and spot any of them.

Meanwhile Kuka parray who had won the election and he was now MLA of sonawari constituency and was busy in a try to enlarge the party and make it more successful but due to the power KUKA and his men had sort of acquired, became his enemy which KUKA had started realizing,

He would get every information about what his men were doing behind his back. The killings, kidnapping and extortion which was done by his men would often put PARRAY in worry but every time KUKA would get information about the deeds of his men it would have been already late.

Same like KUKA wasn't happy with what Rashid Billa had done in Saderkoot, but Rashid had stopped his speed and started acting responsibily now after KUKA had expressed his aggression towards the actions he had done.

But with Fayaz Nawbadi's case KUKA was very worried as did not seemed to be slowing a bit, day after day one or another, deeds of Fayaz Nawbadi's had was putting Parray in worry and he had started making Fayaz Nawbadi realize that.

Fayaz wouldn't listen to Parray as every other his men obeyed his orders as it looked like after coming out of jail Fayaz needed power and weapon to fulfil his personal enmity with HM, which he had got now from Parray, and he would kill HM militants like he was hunting the wild animals, he wouldn't just kill the person he would be as brutal as hell.

Fayaz was one of the commander who was slipping off KUKA's hands and had got him out of control now Fayaz would kill anyone ruthlessly in the name of KUKA parray and Ikhwan.

The path KUKA had taken had now put Kashmir's faith on stake. After making Fayaz understand about the political limitations and party reputation still Fayaz wouldn't listen a word and would kill people on his will not for KUKA Parray, which wasn't good at all for the future of Awami league (KUKA'S POLITICAL PARTY).

KUKA realized that the dreaded force of Ikhwani's around 1000-1200 gunmen's he had put in Kashmir to counter the HM militants were now killing civilians for different reasons more than the militants.

After the killings in asham Parray warned Fayaz not to do more actions like that and he seemed to agree with Parray until, one day KUKA got information about Fayaz killing some of the civilians which KUKA had already warned Fayaz not to do any more killings but Fayaz wouldn't listen a word.

Now was the time when tough decision was about to be in action. After trying to make Fayaz understand many times but he would do the same thing other day, he was so dreadful that whenever he would kill a militant he would make sure that he kills every person whoever had helped those militants to hide out. The killings Fayaz had done was not so easy to justify for Kuka to the government as now there was an elected government in the state and things were being bring back to normal where every incident was being reported by police and in some cases investigation was being started and this all was not a good thing for Parray's political party future,

Fayaz who was totally out of control now was roaming on streets like king, like he had no one he had to answer, he wouldn't fear the God in addiction of his AK 47 of riffle. He had some of his close trusted men because of that HM tried to take him down many times but they failed every time.

One day he was going somewhere with his men's in his jeep and he was blown up in an IED blast in Sumbal, just a few kilometres away from where he had shot Nazima. According to locals the intensity of the blast was such that his body parts could be seen hanging from the power supply wires. Many people believe that he was killed by his own people – the Ikhwani's, by the order of KUKA.

Fayaz who had survived 18 attempts on life finally met his fate on Feb 17, 2000.

Fayaz Nawabadi is considered a martyr and a hero in his village. So are the other Nawabadis killed in these years. Their graveyard reads Mazar-e-Shohada. Fayaz's grave is decorated and fenced. It lies on way to the shrine of a saint in the mohalla, called Sayeed Sahib. A stone throw's distance from the graveyard is a model school. His house has a 12 foot high wall topped by barbed wire. He is survived by two wives and four children.

"Even though almost all the notorious Nawabadis were killed, the people of the surrounding areas cannot forget the mayhem inflicted by them," says Afzal, who happened to meet a relative of Waseem on return from the mohalla. Their response was, "There is no question of forgiveness. Even if they repent it, nothing is going to change. There can be no forgiveness."

Mehraj a resident of Ganderbal:- was a child when the Nawabadis were at the peak of their power. He remembers a day when Nawabadis converged on his village, and cut down all the willow and poplar trees on the government land. "They sold it to their own friends at the cheapest possible rates," he says adding that the fear was such that no government official either resisted or complained of the incident. Such was the case with all of the area. "They even cut trees in the Jarokha Bagh," says Yasin another resident of the area, "Loot was a common thing with Nawabadis those days."

Yasir a local: "Any vehicle which plied from the area was looted. People would think twice before passing through the area dominated by renegades." Sidiq accepts.(Fayaz 's father) "The people from the surrounding areas on the directives of militants had imposed a blockade on us. So we had no option left but to loot for survival." But according to Gulzar from Sumbal, "Nawabadis have always had a bad image in the area. They were involved in thefts and robberies before they became associated with counter-insurgency. After that they would carry out their activities openly. Extortion became their main business."

Chapter 5

Wafadar Khan

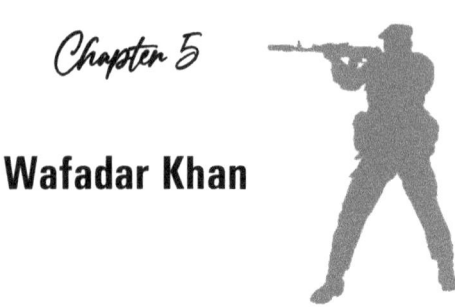

KUKA and Ikhwan was in peak of its power, why would they not be, they now had killed almost 150 HM militants in Kashmir and it was so terrifying and changed situation here even locals were not allowed to perform the final prayer (Jinaza) of the dead militants as I mentioned earlier.

It was the same area where militancy and movement of freedom of Kashmir had started but now the air has changed its direction as it always does. HM had great influence among people during the beginning of the freedom movement however because of some incidents actually a lots of incidents where HM killed a lot of people for lot of reasons and after JKLF outfit exposed the hidden aim of HM merging Kashmir with Pakistan was a turnaround movement in Kashmir. Which was the exact reason behind the growing enmity among these two major militant groups.

Right before the elections of 1996. It was very important for Indian Government to stand a local political party and local face to revive election process so in hands with Kuka parray and central government they called Farooq Abdullah back from London to fight election again in Kashmir for CM chair and convinced him about the situation being in control by government backed outfit Ikhwan and Indian Army.

It had been almost eight years now when Kashmir had its last election and it was the first time in history Farooq Abdulla comes to Hajan for election rally. While addressing the people, first time in Kashmir the pro Indian slogans were raised at that high scale.

Farooq Abdulla during the rally.

Farooq :- mere pyare bhaiyo and behno main national conference ka sadr Farooq abdulla aaj Hajan main isliye aaya hu k aap logu ko yaad dilavu k hum Kashmiri aman pasand log chain se jeena chahte hai.

Aur saath saath main yeh yaad diladu k jinaab sheikh Abdulla mere walid sahab ne Hindustan se dosti isliye nhi ki thi Kashmir main khoon kharaba ho, isliye nhi ki thi k hamare Kashmiri bhai behen apne gharu se be ghr ho balki isliye ki thi k Kashmir main aman o sukoon kayam ho aur main apko batadu Hindustan aaj bhi uss wade pe qayam hai yeh to Pakistan hai jo militants bejke hamara aman o sukoon cheenna chahte hai.

Ab aap hi bataye kya aap aman nhi chahte, kya aap khushi Khushi apne aal o ayaal ke saath nhi rehna chahte agar chahte hai to main aapse wada karta hu k aisa zaroor hoga hum Kashmir main aman paida karenge. Agar aap sab mere saath sehmat hai to mere naara lagaye.

AZAAAAAAAAD HINDOOSTAN

And the crowd shouts with the flow,

AZAAAAAAAAD HINDOOSTAN

NAARAAYEEEE TAKBEEEER

ALLAHO AKBAR

It was the siren for change and disaster finally elections were conducted and Farooq Abdulla won and became the Chief Minister of Jammu and Kashmir again.

While KUKA parray also won the election from his constituency and became MLA of sonawari.

The power and the mission were going side by side Kumar's promise was fulfilled and now it was KUKA Parray's turn to fulfil his.

Kukka Parray during the election campaign in 1996 elections. Pic: Agencies

The picture above was captured during the election campaign in 1996.

Out of many of his dreaded commanders one among them was very different, long hair, bullet belt wrapped on shoulders and a Gun mostly AK 47 in hand. When he used to walk on roads with this style he would look exactly like a Hindi movie Hero, he was none other than Manzoor parray aka WAFADAR KHAN (Kuka's nephew ,his elder brothers son).

There are many stories about how Wafadar would heroically go to fight with militants and sometimes would alone for encounters too.

Wafadar was given the area of Hajan so he was very famous among the people. The people of Hajan would have a silent respect for him. He was like a person among the gangsters who would signify the heroic character. He was kind a jolly character like truthful brave friendly guy.

Whenever Wafadar would patrol through the village though being on side of people who would often kill for their will. Wafadar always would have that different impact, the heroic impact on people, he wasn't involved in most of the civilian killings.

After winning the election KUKA got very busy and the power which was laid on roads were giving nightmares to people.

It wasn't easy to handle more than a thousand gun men's without any systematic disciplined way so the consequences were about to hit the floor.

After all commanders and other Ikhwani's who got areas divided among them started doing things without keeping KUKA in loop and that was the first nail to the coffin.

Ikhwani's were killing militants at an uncountable speed.

Here Wafadar got some conflicts with KUKA with some over the decisions of Hajan. The fear among people exactly look a Hindi movie villain coming to village where no one dares to confront him or his men.

next day Wafadar and his close gun men's were in Hajan market talking to people and warning them if they are going to go against him and then he said loudly and angrily "tomorrow I am going to kill KUKA parray I will wipe him out"

And this was the statement which caught fire till it reached to KUKA.

Many people say when he said this KUKA was passing by. It was coincidence or purposely God knows what it was.

Next day 21 June 1998 WAFADAR was coming home from Srinagar and his car was blown up by a mine blast near wasikhan asham.

Till now more than 160 ikhwani's had been killed but still there was an army of them left to give an any Pro Pakistan militant groups a tough fight.

While this all were happening Indian forces like CRPF,BSF and Indian Army had kept themselves aside as their job was getting done by someone else without putting a needle tip like effort so show was going on and they were watching it.

Almost all HM militants were killed and whoever was left went underground it looked like militancy would never come back again to Kashmir, that much KUKA PARRAY crushed Hizbul Mujahideen and other small groups.

The local people who had a little soft corner still left in their hearts for militants, why little because Hizbul Militants also killed a lot of civilians during the fight between them and Ikhwan and Army. So it wasn't kind of choice left for people that they choose a side now. Every organisation was powerful accept the local civilians who were crushed from time to time by the conflict.

Chapter 6

Gh Rasool Parray aka Kaakh

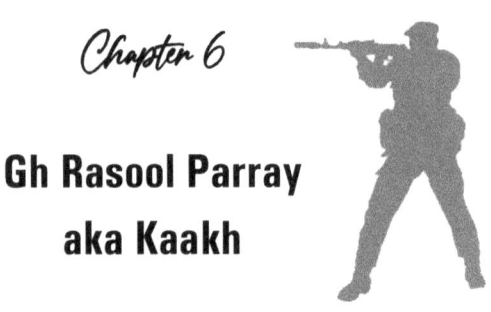

KUKA now had become so powerful that even his far away relatives would roam on roads with the pride of a king like life and authority. He had two more brothers GH AHMAD PARRAY aka AMM PARRAY and GH RASOOL PARRAY aka KAAKH.

GH AHMAD PARRAY was a man with principles he was a responsible person with respect in village, He was kind of sarpanch (not official) in village who would listen to people's issues and would try to solve them as villagers would respect his decisions no one would go against his given decision regarding particular issue not because people were afraid but out of respect.

But the other elder brother of KUKA GH RASOOL aka KAAKH was so aggressive and antagonistic man in village that people would often try to avoid the way he is coming in front.

Though he never carried the Gun but was more dreadfull than a gunmen with AK47 he would roam around with some ikhwani gun men always with as a security. He was very famous in villages like baniyari mukdamyari and adjoining areas which are located on the banks of Wular lake. KUKA himself was not that famous among the people of these villages as much KAAKH was. It was the time when you expect Ikhwani gun men's anytime at your home despite of your links and any other business with them, they would often go to any ones home for dinner and the local people had to cook for them and consider them the guest of hour though if you don't have anything to feed your family you have to feed the gun men's there is no choice in that or else you have to be ready for their aggression which would often end with some ones death.

KAAKH often used to put a chair in Hajan market and everyone passing by has to offer a salaam to him if you don't then your fortune will be decided by him. he was also responsible to gather the people on a rally day KUKKA often used to take people force fully from homes and would gather them in Hajan market then would transport the via buses to wherever the rally has to take place and he was very sharp with it he would know every house hold and the names of head of the family. His hukka was his partner he would take it where ever he would go even in middle of the market he used to put the setup for hukka for him and his associates.

He technically never took a gun but his men's would kill anyone on his will as he was known as the second commander in chief and no one would utter a word against him because he was KUKA'S elder brother and no one still dares to say a word against.

The smart man Dilawar was leading the pack as he would give them different ideas for managing the money. As I earlier said it was Dilawar idea to cut down the willow trees of local forest area which surrounds the Hajan town so that he can arrange money to keep Ikhwan financially strong. After they cut down millions of trees they didn't stop here they let their close people mostly locals from town cut the trees and sell them in market.

After they started kidnapping and extortion they would also live a fun life out of it. All commanders and their associates in different villages started harassing people for money and sometimes they would kill someone just to keep fear alive and to prove the point that if anyone goes against them then this is what is going to happen to them.

Here after the victory in election KUKA was a MLA and had to deal with officials now he often would love to go to Mumbai and have some sea food and would love the beaches and ocean.

Sometimes KUKA had no idea what his associates were doing in local areas that is when he had started losing the pack there had been many incidents when his gun men's disobeyed his orders. They killed lot of people which KUKA would have never wanted them to kill.

In the political market Farooq Abdullah who was the current CM was not that great friends with KUKA but due to compulsion and the only way to be in political power he had to listen to KUKA parray and his ideology because KUKA parray was the main man to contact in Indian central government. Besides Farooq Abdullah kept his political party away from Parray's party Awami League. He continuously gave support to Mohammad Akbar lone who lost election against Parray in Sonawari Constituency.

Parray's men would often raise slogans against Akbar lone and his party whenever they would pass by any national conference worker or Akbar lone himself they would always say.

Yaa peer dastgeer
Albaane dub pher.
And sometimes
Mahboobea
Hea
sinn kya ronuth
badam goje
Parray saebun
foje aaey

While Akbar lone was preparing for next election against Parray, though he had to face the defeat but he was very dedicated to it, the reason could be the support he would get from national conference Farooq Abdullah.

One day Akbar lone crossed paths with Parray on Markundal crossing and the gun men of parray started raising slogans against national conference and Akbar lone which resulted in a small fight between the supporters of both the parties, the fight got so heated up now parray got off from the car and an argument started parray snatched the AK47 from one of his men and cocked it to get ready to fire but one of his men just pushed and turned the barrel of gun other side and one round was fired which missed just some inches from Lone's head and Parray's men managed to take parray aside and got into the car. After this incident Akbar would mostly stay at Srinagar only he wouldn't come home (Naidkhai) frequently which is very close to Hajan.

There was a political war, alliances with central government even its said that parray was the only MLA from Kashmir who met George Walker Bush who was the president of United states of America that time regarding the Kashmir issue. KUKA had become so important to Indian central government now and KUKA was himself looking forward to be in politics but the men he had left without restraint was a big thing to handle more than 1000 men with AK47 riffles that too in the age when mobile phone and internet was not introduced.

According to an interview taken by Rediff.com KUKA who had come long way now with different ideology than what he believed when he had picked up the arms for the freedom of Kashmir with the support of Pakistan. There were some tough questions and most daring ones to ask the person like KUKKA by the interviewer they were like

Pakistan has been aiding and abetting cross-border terrorism in the name of supporting the Kashmiri cause.

Everyone in the world knows that Pakistan has a hidden agenda behind the so-called jihad for the Kashmiri cause. I can tell you Pakistan only wants the land of Jammu and Kashmir minus the Kashmiris. The sooner the people of Kashmir realise this the better it would be.

Do you believe that the assembly election in Jammu and Kashmir should be held under governor's rule?

I definitely support this move. Because the present government of Jammu and Kashmir cannot be trusted. The people of Jammu and Kashmir should not only participate in the election but we must also ensure that only those *[votes]* which are cast by the people of the state come out of the boxes. People have lost faith in the present government.

But the 1996 election was held under governor's rule. What went wrong then?

It is true that the election in the state were held under governor's rule in 1996 and the National Conference swept to power. The people were happy that an elected government had come to power and the new rulers would take care of their needs. But what did Dr Farooq Abdullah do for the people of Jammu and Kashmir? You go and meet the people and they will tell you how angry they are with him. He has not done anything for the people of Kashmir. So much so that even the political parties have lost faith in him. That is why we want to have elections under governor's rule.

Will you participate in the election?

Of course, we will participate in the election. We participated in the 1996 election when most of the political parties were scared to contest the election.

I was one of those who can take credit for holding an election in Jammu and Kashmir in 1996. I lost a number of men during the election campaign. I have so far lost more than 600 surrendered militants who had joined hands with me in counter-insurgency operations against terrorists operating in Kashmir. The present government of Jammu and Kashmir is a dangerous government.

Why can't you have a free and fair election under Dr Abdullah's government?

Free and fair elections have been a major problem in Jammu and Kashmir. If we look at the rest of the Indian states then we will find that citizens of those states have a right to vote. This right is not being extended to the state of Jammu and Kashmir. If free and fair polls are held in the state then all those who are feeling alienated will come back to the mainstream. If that happens then it would be for the good of the country. But if that happens then President's rule should also be extended to the state of Gujarat. You have seen how the minority community was treated by the administration in the last few months. Because elections are scheduled to be held in Gujarat as well.

Why have you described the National Conference as a dangerous party?

Dr Farooq Abdullah's government has betrayed the people of Jammu and Kashmir. The rulers are plundering the state development money. Instead of using the money for the welfare of the people they simply pocket the money and use it for their personal ends. Ministers in the Abdullah government have bought properties not only in Srinagar, Jammu but also in Delhi.

There is another aspect to this. The major political parties are getting their rivals killed for the sake of getting some electoral gains here and there.

I have been asking the people of Jammu and Kashmir to participate in the state election. I have held several major rallies in Jammu and Srinagar in recent weeks. I have even asked the Hurriyat Conference to take part in the electoral process.

Pakistan claims they are the true supporters of the people of Kashmir.

Ask those who are living in so-called Azad Kashmir. The Mirpuris and the rest. Their plight is worse than us. I would say we are far better off than Kashmiris living across the Line of Control. We have got letters from those people who have been pleading with the Government of India to free them from Pakistan's clutches.

Kashmir is the crown of India. It would remain so in future as well. I would say the people of Kashmir would sacrifice anything to retain this crown with India.

Jamaat-i-Islami leader Syed Ali Shah Geelani claims a merger with Pakistan is the ultimate solution to the Kashmir problem.

Who is he to decide what is good for the people of Kashmir? He has been misleading young Kashmiris to take up guns in the name of jihad. But if you look at him, you will find that his sons and daughters have had a good education in the best of Indian schools. They are doing well in life. He has been totally exposed. People of the state know he has been misleading the people of Kashmir. They know his policies are anti-Kashmir and they do not want to follow him.

There are times when it is alleged that your men have indulged in looting and extortion. Is that true?

I categorically deny that any of my men have ever indulged in looting and extortion. I would like to tell you that the National Conference has a large number of trained youth who go by the name of surrendered militants and they indulge in extortion etc. They do the bad work and my organisation gets a bad name. Some of them work with the Border Security Force, some with the Jammu and Kashmir Police and the rest with the Special Task Force. My men are a disciplined lot and do not indulge in crime.

There were some bitter truths hidden in this interview which parray revealed, of course it was a political interview which had to be a bit diplomatic but there were a lot of things going at the side, KUKA was right about many things happening in Kashmir, the name PARRAY had become so big that anyone would use it for their personal benefits like other party workers would go to Srinagar to loot local people in the name of PARRAY, for the political rivalries also, while parray had no information who is doing what on his name which was creating hatred for PARRAY among locals. it was not only KUKA who was playing an important role in the current situation there were many people with different ideologies playing their part, if we through timeline since 1993 a lot of continuous changes were seen in Kashmir in terms of the Kashmir conflict is concern and it was like.

In 1993 All Parties Hurriyat Conference (APHC) is formed. It is an amalgamation of dozens of Kashmiri political groups. Its express goal is Kashmir's "right to self-determination" but keeps the question of independence or merger with Pakistan open. As armed movement continues, Indian military repression grows. In response to a JKLF attack in northern Kashmiri town of Sopore in **January**, Indian paramilitary Border Security Force (BSF) massacres more than 100 unarmed civilians and burns down several neighbourhoods. In **April**, a prominent Kashmiri heart surgeon and JKLF sympathizer, Abdul Ahad Guru, is shot dead. (Later a key Indian bureaucrat in Kashmir, Wajahat Habibullah, will blame Indian security agencies to have conspired with an HM activist to kill Guru.) In **October**, BSF kills 55 Kashmiris who had assembled after Friday prayers in Bijbehara town in South Kashmir. Despite several accords, intergroup rivalry leads to frequent clashes between the JKLF and the HM. Better trained HM cadres kill dozens of JKLF members.

In 1994 On February 22, the Indian Parliament passes a resolution that claims Kashmir to be an "integral part" of

India and therefore non-negotiable. More forces are sent to Kashmir to subdue the armed insurgency and to conduct elections. In May, JKLF commander Yasin Malik, on bail from prison, declares a unilateral ceasefire and claims JKLF to be an unarmed political organization that would work for independence of Kashmir. His decision causes a split in the JKLF. One JKLF faction refuses to declare a ceasefire, but its leaders are quickly decimated by Indian forces during a siege in Srinagar. In June, former MUF legislator and head preacher of South Kashmir, Qazi Nisar, is shot dead in Islamabad/Anantnag. Many blame the HM. Pan-Islamic groups like Harkat ul Mujahideen are also now present in parts of Kashmir. With JKLF no longer a competitor, HM targets members of smaller groups.

In 1995 Foreign armed mujahideen, especially those aligned with Harkat ul Mujahideen (later Harkat ul Ansar) become a formidable force in the Kashmir war. Their goals are unclear, but their presence causes further confusion. They claim to be fighting a jihad, yet some of them seem to be collaborating with the Ikhwan/MM. On July 4, a faction of Harkat, known as Al Faran, kidnaps five western tourists in South Kashmir and after several months—as revealed later by journalists Adrian Levy and Cathy Scott in their book *The Meadow*—hands them over to an MM commander, who is believed to have killed them.

In 1996 On March 8, prominent Kashmiri human rights activist and lawyer Jalil Andrabi is abducted by an Indian military officer Avtar Gill. Andrabi's body is later recovered from a river.

In 1997 Under intense pressure from the Ikhwanis, Jamaat Islami declares end to ties with the HM. HM launches systematic attacks on the Ikhwanis and decimates them. HM returns to dominance in the countryside, but Indian military has also regained enormous ground.

In 1998 On January 25, 23 Kashmiri Hindus are killed in a massacre in Wandhama village. India blames Islamist militants. In two other incidents, in Prankot and Champanari in Jammu, several Hindus are killed in April and June. Insurgency spreads to the Muslim districts of Jammu province. In the Kashmir valley, the Indian counterinsurgency war continues. Hundreds of Kashmiris are killed year after year. In May, India and Pakistan conduct nuclear tests.

In 1999 War between India and Pakistan breaks out in Kargil, a border district on the LoC. India blames Pakistani soldiers for infiltrating into positions on the Indian controlled side of the LoC. Hundreds of soldiers die in the battles. By July, international pressure compels Pakistan to withdraw its forces. Pakistan PM Nawaz Sharif accuses General Pervez Musharraf of launching the operation without informing the government.

The Pakistani politics had always been on hurdles and full of confusions about who is more powerful and gets to decide, Army General or Prime Minister which is till date one of the reason why Pakistan is not developing economically or being recognised and trustworthy by most of the countries in the world.

In Pakistan whatever the future plans and steps Prime Minister decides they never get along with their Army General or if they get along, then militant outfits are always seeing Pakistan's future in different way, And that is exactly when Kashmir gets trouble, it doesn't matter who ever is conducting the election India or Pakistan the Kashmir issue is used for the vote bank. For Kashmir it has always been very difficult to decide the air here changes the colour very often. well it is actually difficult to bring stability at a place especially place like Kashmir which is surrounded by three nuclear power countries which is India, Pakistan and China and all of them want Kashmir be there's for ever.

During the Ikhwan rule in Kashmir there were hundreds of un reported incidents every village had a famous Ikhwani militants who were famous with their nick names for example

- Ajas (a village of sonawari tehsil) area had D BAAND who was so monstrous that people would say that if someone would fail to do what he had asked mostly money they would ask. He would kidnap some kid from the family and would kill him and then he used to take out all his internal organs and he would pack it in polythene and send it to their parents. So that next time no one dare to take them for granted.

- In Suderkoot bala (a village of sonawari tehsil) Rashid billa was famous especially after he killed 31 people of same evening when he massacred Gh Qadir Dar's family, He looked very handsome cleanshaved with a small mustache guy but was very inhuman.

- Hajan (the main town of sonawari tehsil) had Wafadar Khan, Bashir Yar Kaakh and many other as they had headquarters in Hajan, during their presence police or Army would not come to village.

- Gundjahangir (a village of sonawari tehsil) had Qadir Hurra who was local area commander, he was mostly involved in harassing people specially fruit growers of the area because this village is mostly dependent on apple orchards, this area also had some militant background so Qadir Hurra was one of the Ikhwani to deal with it in the area. At Last Qadir was killed by unknown gunmen who came to ask him about matche box they had worn a Pheran (Kashmiri traditional wear, a coat) offered salaam to Hurra and then took out the barrels of AK 47 out of Pheran and started firing at him until he was dead.

- Sumbal (a village of sonawari tehsil) and Srinagar had Fayaz Nawbadi himself, very famous among people many people in Srinagar would not know KUKA PARRAY but everyone knew who Fayaz nawbadi was, as I mentioned earlier killings he was involved in more than 200 civilian killing, KUKA himself was very unhappy with anger which at last took Fayaz Nawbadi life in a mine blast.

Kaakh's daughter Shehnaza was not less than a militant she would often go river to Jhelum for drinking water where all other women were threatened by her, no one would dare to talk to rudely and she would always carry a pistol with her.

These killings and weapons in civilian's hands was a normal thing particularly in Hajan area. People from outside Hajan would think hundred times before visiting to their relatives in Hajan. No father from all other villages would give their daughters hand to any guy from Hajan.

In Srinagar areas who had never seen KUKA Parray physically were easily being fooled by any political party workers they would pretend they we are Parray's men and loot them which KUKA had never been informed of, people would think these are Parray's people but in reality a lot of times they used to be from opposition party workers, some were just normal smart people who used to take advantage of parray's name, they knew that no one was going to parray directly to complain about them.

One more funny thing happened in the political war of National Conference and Awami League (the name of Kuka Parray's political party), the people who were in Ikhwan and harassed thousands of people in the name of Ikhwan and Kuka Parray, those were the same people who joined National Conference later and started giving speeches about how Ikhwan has harassed and killed people of Kashmir. I guess which is also a normal thing when you see Indian politics.

Chapter 7

The Beginning of an End

The so called democracy had returned to Kashmir people had an elected Chief Minister and every Constituency had elected MLA's. Militant appearances were almost at an end. Kashmiri civilians were not joining militant ranks on that high scale in fear of Parray now that it was the time when Ikhwani's had fulfilled their job but with some hundreds of civil casualties. Kumar had done his job perfectly but this time civil causalities crossed the limit. KUKA had started dreaming about the future of Awami league but this ocean of gangsters which he had left in every single village which made it possible to make Kashmir militant free, but now it was being difficult for him to manage these much people who were not a common people but an army of gangsters.

During these years of mess created by all these outfits now it was the time this all was about to end besides this there was a lot going on on internationally.

On March 20 2000 just before US President Bill Clinton's visit to India, 35 Kashmiri Sikhs are killed by unidentified gunmen in the village of Chattisinghpora in South Kashmir. The government blames Islamic militants, but Kashmiris and prominent Sikh leaders (and later US officials) blame Indian government agencies for orchestrating the attack to seek US sympathy. The perception of the Indian role in the massacre becomes reinforced when a few days after the Chattisinghpora massacre, Indian forces abduct, kill, and mutilate the bodies of five local Kashmiris, claiming they are the foreign Islamist militants responsible for killing the Sikhs. A week after, at Brakpora in Islamabad/Anantnag, Indian forces kill nine protestors demanding an impartial investigation. Despite attempts to fudge the DNA by the NC-led government, subsequent tests of the exhumed corpses prove that the five dead "foreign militants" were actually local civilians.

In Kashmir these unknown gunmen has always been a mystery and this mystery was always benefit for every outfit. Anyone gets killed here is forbidden because you don't know who this unknown gunmen is. So militant outfits blame Indian forces to be the unknown gunmen and Indian government officials would always say its Islamic militants who kill these people.

During this time India and Pakistan were continuously trying to hold talks so that they come to a conclusion but world has never been fair to anyone. Power and greed makes the man to commit things which he would never do if it wasn't for power.

In **July** 2001 Indian and Pakistani leaders meet but fail to arrive at a settlement on the Kashmir issue. However, plans for free trade, demilitarization, and shared autonomy in Kashmir are discussed. However, in September, in the wake of the 9/11 attacks in the US, Indian PM Vajpayee requests US President Bush to extend his "War on Terror" to Kashmir as well. The APHC and the JKLF denounce this as opportunistic. The US demands Pakistani support in Afghanistan and declares Pakistan to be a "major non-NATO ally." Pakistan drastically cuts support to Kashmiri groups. After an armed attack on the Indian Parliament in December, which India blames on Pakistan-backed groups Lashkar-e-Tayyiba (LeT) and Jaish-e-Muhammad (JeM) operating in Kashmir, Indian police arrest five Kashmiris, even though all the attackers are dead and are claimed to be from Pakistan. India starts a year-long build-up of military forces on the border, threatening war with Pakistan.

In Kashmir from last few decades on every newspaper the headline remains the same only the body changes with names of the rulers rest everything remains same which is "The solution to Kashmir issue will be done very soon".

KUKA had lost few hundred of his men in this war for India he had been fighting for which was itself a lot to have on his plate. He was desperately looking forward for upcoming elections he now wanted to make this party very strong systematically but there were lot of his close men who at first started leaving his party and started joining national conference, They had smelled the change in air because national conference was publicly showing very aggressive behaviour against KUKA and his party. They would always pick on the killings which were done by the hands of Ikhwani's. KUKA had realized a little that he had done a mistake by leaving his men with all those weapons free in locals.

Now was the time for next big step for KUKA and Awami league party which was the elections of 2002 where KUKA had to taste the defeat and Mohammad Akbar Lone won elections from Sonawari constituency.

KUKA no longer got that much support from Indian central government he sort of felt that India no longer needed KUKA to be in power especially after what chaos Ikhwani's had made. Ikhwani gunmen's slowly started taking their steps back, most of them dropped the weapon and started the normal life. The remnants of the Ikhwani's are absorbed into regular Indian and local police forces.

On May 21 2002 prominent APHC leader, Abdul Ghani Lone, is assassinated by unidentified gunmen. India blames the Pakistani ISI and the hardline factions of the APHC, while many in Kashmir blame Indian agencies. In October, former Indian Home Minister of Kashmiri origin, Mufti Syed, and his newly-created Peoples Democratic Party (PDP), win elections and form a coalition government with the Indian Congress. PDP ran its campaign on the idea of establishing "self-rule" in Kashmir. NC ran on the promise of re-establishing the pre-1953 "autonomy" for Kashmir.

Hajan and adjoining areas got little bit calm after the elections. People started doing their regular work now no longer you could see gun men's on civil dresses roaming on streets, but fear was still in the air, the gun culture had taken a back seat but you could still hear the firing shots of AK47 in your head. Every street every corner would tell a story what it had faced silently. After this defeat KUKA's closed men started leaving him they started joining national conference openly as they had now the clear idea that KUKA would not retreat.

Now not many of his men were left, the power he possessed, was gone, even the people who had given this mission to him were not showing an expectable support to him after seeing his empire which had created in those years falling apart Parray had got kind of exhausted and he just went with the flow. Losing the power and importance day by day this had put Parray and his associates in little worry as they all were aware what mess their outfit had created and what could be the consequences especially after losing the power in assembly, now someone else was owning the power.

Jammu and Kashmir National Conference was the single largest party but lacked majority. The Jammu and Kashmir People's Democratic party (PDP) and the Indian National Congress (Congress) formed a coalition government with PDP's Mufti Mohammad Syed serving as the Chief Minister for the first three years and Congress's Ghulam Nabi Azad for the next three years. The election saw a major boycott at the appeal of Tehreek-e-Hurriyat. Kashmir division had a voting percentage of

3.5% while Jammu division had a voting percentage of 16.5%.Rajouri district recorded the least voting percentage at 2.7% The Panther's Party formed part of the ruling coalition with Harsh Dev Singh as the party's first cabinet minister.

Now again the power had changed its course now new people in power, dealing with the situation according to their ideologies despite of knowing what has happened already everyone would blame the earlier rulers to gain sympathy among people to stay in power. The history of Kashmir has been very complicated that is why its referred as the most dangerous place on earth. The prospect of two nuclear powers facing off across such a comparatively small space is frightening indeed. Since the partition of India and Pakistan in 1947, this unresolved land and the people who live there have been at the root of constant tension between the world's most populous democracy, India, and its neighbour Pakistan. Three major wars have been fought between those protagonists over the years only heightens the fear that now exists given their advanced technology. Global and regional implications aside, the instability and lack of any conclusive resolution to the political dispute have left the population of Kashmir divided and uncertain about their future. A land of immense beauty, Kashmir has seen its once burgeoning tourist industry fade completely in the face of military incursions and militant activity.

Parray was constantly losing the men, even his close friend DILAWAR had betrayed him he had joined hands with national conference and that is what exactly the real face of politics they leave you when they see you losing power and majority, now power and money both were slipping off hands so he decided to approach the central government who he had been friends with long time now.

But one more thing why Parray himself was liked by so many people after even all this bloodshed his men had done was because of the glimpse of principles and helping poor people nature in his character, he would reflect the character of Karim Lala and Haji Mastaan (Bombay's biggest Gangsters of 80's who were very kind to poor people)

Parray at his residence at Hajan.

KUKA to his one of the associate: Kumar ko khabar bejo unhe bolo parray se milne ke liye jald se jald aaye

KUKA's associate: ji jinaab main itilah bijwadeta hun.

He gets in contact with some officials as Kumar is not a publicly known government officer he is still a secret RAW agent.

Next day KUKA gets in touch with Kumar and sets a meeting Kumar was still underground in Kashmir working closely with Intelligence bureau (IB) and Research Analysis Wing (RAW) which was his primary department.

Next day Kumar arrives at KUKA's Residence for meeting

KUKA with his associates already present in room when Kumar arrives.

KUMAR: Adaab jinaab parray sahab kaise hai aap, bahut arsa hogaya hai ab aapko dekhe huve tabiyat wagaira theek haina aapki.

KUKA: ji sab khairiyat se hai bas aapse milna zaruri samja isliye aapko takleef di

KUMAR: takleef ki kya baat hai ismain aap hamare bahut purane dost hai aap se milne ke liye hum kabhi mana karsakte hai kya. Baaki hamare liye koi hukum ho to bataye, hum aapke liye kya karsakte hai.

KUKA: jinaab aapse kuch mushwara karna chahte the isliye aapse milna zaruri tha.

KUMAR: ji boliye kya chahte hai aap humse hum bilkul aapke liye hamesha se tyaar hai, bas aap boliye kya pareshaani hai.

KUKA: Kashmir ke kya haal hai aapko to sab pata hi hai ab aapse kya chupa hai. Maine jo aapse wada kiya tha woh maine poora kiya Kashmir ko militancy se Azaad karake election system wapas bahaal karke diya hai, lekin badkismati se main yeh election haar gaya.

Dekhiye main aapse bas kehna chahta hu k jo bhi causualities huvi hai woh bas halaat ka takaza tha, itna khoon kharaba to nhi chahte the lekin ab ek poore mulk se ladne ke liye itne saare hadisaat hogaye usmain kya hi karsakte the. Sab kuch hamare haath main bhi nhi tha.

Ek side se Hizbul mujahideen dusre side se huriyat conference aur JKLF kitni siyasi aur gher siyasi tanzeeme se ladna pada idr.

Bas ab baat itni si hai k jo support centeral government ne pehle dikhaya tha woh bas bana rahe. Aap ko to pata hi hai k yeh sab jo bhi tha Kashmir ko Pakistan ke behkawe se nikalne ke liye kitna zaruri tha.

KUMAR: parray sahab main sab samjta hu aapki baat aur apse bilkul sehmat hu lekin aap yeh bhi to samjye k aapki tanzeem walu ne civil casualities hadd se bahut zyada ki hai. Senkdu main log maare gaye hai aur khaas kar Kashmir main jo nayi government bani hai woh iss baat ka fayda hamesha uthayengi election ke time ho ya baaki aam rallies unko kaise rokenge, main phir bhi baat karta hu Sarkar se dekhta hu main kya kar sakta hu aapke liye. Baaki aap bilkul parwa na kijiye sab theek hoga.

KUKA: shukriya uskle liye main bilkul samjta hu k Ikhwan se logu ko takleef to huvi hai ab kisi ne mera naam apne fayde ke liye use kiya lekin ab uski zimadaari to meri hi banti hai. Theeek hai aap dekhiye aapse kya hosakta hai baaki main ab apni political party continue rakhuga ab agle election main dekhte hai, ladenge zarur aur jeet ke dikhayenge.

KUMAR: theek hai jinaab ab mujhe ijazat dijiye main jaata hu, aur haan Kashmir main ab bhi militancy poori tarah se nhi saaf huvi hai, balki ab to aapke haarne se woh aur zor main aagaye hai aapke bahut logu pe hamla bhi ho rha hai maine suna.

KUKA: hamle to hamesha se hote aaye hai mere aadmiyu pe bas ab hum wapas kuch nhi karsakte hai bas takleef itni hai, mere to aajtak 300 se zyada aadmi militants ke haathu maare jachuke hai. Bas ab aap dekhye is cheez ko kaise sambala jaye kyunki ab mere pass woh log to nhi hai jo unka jawaab desakte hai.

KUMAR: theek hai main dekhta hu kya karsakte hai is baare main.

Kumar leaves the place and disappears.

During this tenure Indian politics had also seen lots of ups and downs also according to the history lime published in BBC report.

1991 - Rajiv Gandhi assassinated by suicide bomber sympathetic to Sri Lanka's Tamil Tigers.

1991 - Economic reform programme begun by Prime Minister PV Narasimha Rao.

1992 - Hindu extremists demolish mosque in Ayodhya, triggering widespread Hindu-Muslim violence.

1996 - Congress suffers worst ever electoral defeat as Hindu nationalist BJP emerges as largest single party.

1998 - BJP forms coalition government under Prime Minister Atal Behari Vajpayee.

Tensions over Kashmir have brought India and Pakistan to war

1998 - India carries out nuclear tests, leading to widespread international condemnation.

1999 February - Mr Vajpayee makes historic bus trip to Pakistan to meet Premier Nawaz Sharif and signs bilateral Lahore peace declaration.

1999 May - Tension in Kashmir leads to brief war with Pakistan-backed forces in the icy heights around Kargil in Indian-held Kashmir.

2000 May - India marks the birth of its billionth citizen.

2001 - A high-powered rocket is launched, propelling India into the club of countries able to fire big satellites deep into space.

Disputed Siachen, dubbed the world's highest battlefield

2002 January - India successfully test-fires a nuclear-capable ballistic missile - the Agni - off its eastern coast.

2002 February - Inter-religious bloodshed breaks out after 59 Hindu pilgrims returning from Ayodhya are killed in a train fire in Godhra, Gujarat. More than 1,000 people, mainly Muslims, die in subsequent violence.

There was a lot going on from nuclear tests from both countries to violence reported in other states besides that Kashmir looked bit stable than earlier so Indian central government had not put Kashmir now in its priority list.

The mission which was started by Kumar with KUKA parray in Kashmir with the direct help of central government was now dumped like a report under the dust covered files in some corner of the room. Because of lot of changes in Indian politics no one really recognised the mission which was the most important one in the history of Kashmir.

Kumar went to Delhi to meet prime minister regarding the issue.

But the air had taken different sides to blow on the face of India and its system.

Due to the recent bloodshed seen in Gujrat Indian government was very worried, expecting riots in coming days. Even Pakistan had now openly presented themselves a nuclear power country which was not a good news for India at all.

There in Pakistan Syed Sallahu din was again seen in actively working and giving arms and ammunition training to new recruitments. He kept making Hizbul Mujahideen stronger and stronger day by day and wouldn't stop sending guirella force to Kashmir for fighting for the cause of merging Pakistan with Kashmir.

Kashmir's beauty has always attracted trouble and that is the exact reason Kashmir has suffered a lot.

When Kumar came back to PM office and finally managed to set meeting with Prime Minister but this time, time had changed its course.

PM office.

KUMAR to **PM**: Good Morning Sir

PM: Good Morning Mr. Kumar how are you,

KUMAR: I am good sir, thank you

PM: Tell me what is so urgent what is the reason you called the meeting.

KUMAR: Sir, I am very sorry I called this meeting urgently, But the reason is very important.

PM: please go on, tell me, what is so important that RAW's best officer is so worried about.

KUMAR: Sir the reason is Kashmir and KUKA PARRAY.

PM: what happened in Kashmir I thought you would be worried about Gujrat this time.

KUMAR: Sir Gujrat is also priority but there we can manage but in Kashmir it's not the same that has to be on top priority.

PM: ok so tell me what are we talking about.

KUMAR: Sir, Kashmir as you know in 1996 we were able to conduct elections after almost 9 years that all was possible because of one man which is KUKA PARRAY he helped Indian Army to neutralize and wiped out almost every militant from Kashmir, but now the time has changed. KUKA PARRAY as you he participated in 1996 elections and won from Sonawari Constituency, but in 2002 elections he was defeated by national conference member Mohammad Akbar lone, which was not the problem at all but due to the war between Ikhwan ul muslimoon and Hizbul Mujahideen who were crushed down to earth by Parray. But parray lost about 300 men in this war between both of the outfits, Now after Parray's defeat, Hizbul Mujahideen is growing roots again in Kashmir which is not good for us at all,

PM: I have lots of issues to deal right now should I handle Gujrat or do I put my focus in Kashmir.

KUMAR: Sir Kashmir is very important to put focus on, you have elected government in Gujrat from your party only we can handle that, but if we don't put our focus on Kashmir right now all the hard work of these year will go in vain.

PM: ok tell me what you want me to do.

KUMAR: I want you to continue your support to KUKA parray, he has done so much for India already and he has potential to do more. Hizbul Mujahideen is growing and covering villages in Kashmir. We have to Support Parray and continue this war against the militants in Kashmir if we want to Kashmir to be with India forever.

PM: But Kumar you know what you are saying, last time because of this KUKA Parray and his men's hundreds of civil **casualties** occurred in Kashmir, Kashmir is under its own constitution we have to be answerable Human Rights and to the High Court of Jammu and Kashmir when these all cases will be filed right now if people aren't filing FIR's that doesn't mean they will forget these killings.

And also whoever the Prime Minister approved this kind of step is not in power to take responsibility, if anything goes sideways now I have to be responsibility for it, after your mission in Kashmir was approved nothing has remained same in India Prime Minister changed three times and the situation in 1993 and 2002 is very different I cant approve more bloodshed in Kashmir, we have more than half a million soldiers in Kashmir let them handle it.

KUMAR: but sir this is very important otherwise we may lose Kashmir again, Hizbul Mujahideen may take over, they are spreading all over.

PM: tell me one thing, how many Hizbul Mujahideen militants you think would be active in Kashmir right now.

KUMAR: almost 300

PM: this number was more than 2000 before 8 years, more than 10000 Kashmiri people had crossed the border, when we overcame that, why can't we handle these 300 Hizbul Mujahideen militants, especially now we have almost 6 lakh soldiers there to handle the situation, Kumar I think you are worrying too much about it, and yes KUKA Parray will get more a battalion CRPF men for the safety for him and his family you don't worry.

But if you think I would approve this civil suicide, you are wrong that is not happening, I don't want any civil casualties in Kashmir again. Pakistan is nuclear power country now they always blame us to be forcefully in Kashmir in front of United Nations. I don't want anyone to blame India for any reasons related to Kashmir.

Do one thing let Army handle the remaining militants, I don't know for what reasons earlier Prime minister had allowed all this but this has created mess which needs to be handled carefully otherwise we may lose Kashmir.

Meeting Dispersed.

Kumar left PM office without getting what he expected. He immediately.

Prime Ministers worry was justified as 2002 had been the year of bloodshed and hurdles in the history of the world there was a lot going on according to an article of India currents about the year review was like

The year 2002 will go down in history as a worried year, one in which the majority of Americans were trying to recover from twin shocks: one, the 9/11 events which shook American self-worth more than anything else in recent history, even Vietnam; two, the recession that has extended to almost all sectors of the economy. All in all, a rather depressing year.

Among the headline-grabbing items in the U.S. of greatest relevance to Indian Americans in 2002 were the following:

• The possibility of another war with Iraq. There is fear that war may exacerbate tensions with Europe and the Muslim world, leading to further shocks to the already fragile consumer confidence in the U.S.

• The misdeeds of large corporations such as Enron and Worldcom. Hitherto seen as among the world's most transparent and stockholder friendly firms, the sudden emergence of hanky panky among former stock market darlings such as Enron has been shocking to investors.

• The continuing downturn in the economy and the stock market. As the economy continues to slide, with more interest rate cuts in the offing, competition is beginning to heat up. For instance, the number of H-1B visas granted has dropped drastically, while the number of companies outsourcing software and IT-enabled services to India is going up.

• The murder of Daniel Pearl in Pakistan. In further evidence that Pakistan has now become the source of Islamist terrorism, journalist Daniel Pearl of the Wall Street Journal was kidnapped and murdered.

• The saga of the Virginia sniper. The assault on the safety and security of common folks in the U.S. continued with these seemingly random acts of terror.

• The Republicans' feat of retaining the Senate in mid-term elections. The Republicans managed to keep the Senate. Traditionally largely Democratic, Indian-Americans are taking a long, hard look at whether they need to hedge their bets by raising their profile in the Republican Party as well.

• The defeat of a virulently anti-India Congresswoman. Cynthia McKinney of Georgia lost her seat in the U.S. Congress after a campaign in which her opponent was heavily supported by Indian-Americans. The point will not be lost on other India-bashers like Dan Burton of Indiana.

• The increase in incidents of racial profiling following tough new legislation. As the effects of Homeland Security related measures go into effect, Indian-Americans may find themselves at the receiving end of rude security searches.

There were a number of important events in India that will also affect Indian-Americans or their loved ones back in India.

Politics

• The election of Abdul Kalam as President of India. After fractious and divisive jockeying among all the political parties of the country, it was a positive sign that the apolitical APJ Abdul Kalam was elected President. That this aerospace engineer of humble origins—his family are fisherfolk in Rameswaram, Tamil Nadu—was elevated to the highest constitutional post in the country was a refreshing indicator that indeed it is possible for any child to aspire to the top jobs in the nation.

• The "free and fair" elections in Jammu and Kashmir. Despite many gloomy predictions, a boycott by the separatist Hurriyat alliance, and many acts of violence by Pakistani-aided terrorists, almost half of the eligible electorate in Jammu and Kashmir chose to exercise their franchise in a poll that was widely seen as a referendum on how interested Kashmiris were in staying within the Indian Union. The ruling National Conference were reduced to being the biggest single party, and an alliance of the Congress and a local party, the PDP, came to power.

National Affairs

• Supreme Court decisions on education. In two landmark decisions, comparable to the Brown v. Board of Education civil rights decision in the U.S., India's apex court set the stage for dramatic changes in education. In the first, the court upheld the constitutionality of a newly revised curriculum, with greater emphasis on Indic concepts. In the second, the court held that all communities had an equal right to run their own educational institutions, and that if they were aided by the State they would all be subject to the same criteria. In the past, the majority community had been prohibited from running its own schools.

• The carnage in Godhra and Gujarat. After 59 Hindu pilgrims returning from Ayodhya were burned to death by a Muslim mob near Godhra, revenge killings erupted into massive communal riots. The government estimates roughly 850 people were killed, including some 600 Muslims and 200 Hindus and security men.

• The Tamil Nadu Ordinance and Bill on religious conversions. Alarmed by widespread religious conversion of poor Hindus, especially by militant Protestant Christian sects which often use money or other inducements, the Tamil Nadu government issued an ordinance, which was later passed as a bill by the legislature, banning all occurrences of forced conversion as unconstitutional.

• The PIO factor. The Union government has declared Jan. 9 as "Person of Indian Origin" day, and will have a grand gala celebration on that day in 2003. The PIO card, which confers rights including visa-less entry and ownership of real estate, now costs $310 as opposed to $1000 when it was first introduced. The government is still silent on dual citizenship, citing security risks.

Subcontinent

• Troop deployment by India on the Pakistan border. As a result of the attacks on Parliament and on Kaluchak, an army camp where mostly dependents of servicemen were killed, the Indian government ordered a full-fledged troop deployment all along the entire Indo-Pak border. The objective was coercive diplomacy, indicating to Pakistan and the international community that India was fully prepared to go to war if necessary to defend its interests. In many ways, it worked, so that the all-important J&K elections could be held.

• The attacks on Hindu pilgrims at Amarnath and at Akshardham. As part of Pakistan's continuing "war of a thousand cuts" inflicting pain on India, terrorists attacked and killed Hindu pilgrims making the annual pilgrimage to the Amarnath shrine in Kashmir. Later, two terrorists entered the Akshardham temple in Gujarat, killing Hindu worshippers. The intent in both cases was to incite fury among Hindus, leading to retaliatory attacks on Muslims. However, Hindus refused to rise to the bait.

International

• Revelation of Pakistan-North Korea links in missile and nuclear proliferation. American sources announced that Pakistan had been instrumental in North Korea's development of its clandestine nuclear bomb. The quid pro quo, apparently, was the transfer of Korean missile technology (possibly originating in China) to Pakistan.

The proliferation activities of Pakistan and its mentor China should come as no surprise to anyone.

• Gen. Musharraf's speeches promising to eliminate cross-border terrorism. Under substantial pressure from the Americans, and confronted with the Indian Army's mobilization along his borders, Pakistan's dictator made speeches in January and June promising to cut down on cross-border terrorism inflicted on India by his protégés. Unfortunately, he was lying, but Pakistan admitting its guilt was a step forward.

There may be a hundreds of events happening worldwide but India always know the value of Kashmir being its part so Kumar did not get disappointed after Prime Minister not being so helpful regarding the Kashmir. He wanted to save KUKA at any cost, he was the only one who was aware of the value of Parray. Kumar knew that if he failed to provide security to Parray he will be targeted by Hizbul Mujahideen. Because till the date more than 450 had been killed by Ikhwani men's and that was the enough reason for Hizbul Mujahideen to kill Parray and his associates.

more than 400 civilians had also lost their life in this conflict between Militants and Ikhwani's, for Kashmir they were never given a fair choice to choose their sides, first Indian Army forcefully captured Kashmir then to get rid of that JKLF was born for freedom of Kashmir with the support of Pakistan, Then Hizbul Mujahideen headed by Syed Sallah ud din was created with the aim of merging Kashmir with Pakistan, when Kashmiris opposed that then Kashmiri civilian were killed by Hizbul militants then JKLF turned against Hizbul Mujahideen to get rid of pro Pakistani militants, again Kashmiri civilians, Kashmiri pandits in 1989 after that Kashmiri muslims were crushed in between. For Kashmiris the history has been not less than a roller coaster ride till today. Now the issue so much complicated that it is become so hard for everyone to find a possible solution.

Here Kumar was worried about KUKA and his men he didn't want to lose him, He directly left to Kashmir to meet KUKA.

Once he reached at Parray's residence he immediately called Parray and took him along to a room.

KUMAR: Parray main kal hi Prime Minister se mila aapke bare main baat karne ke liye.

KUKA: to kya Prime Minister ab to unko mere koi ehsaan yaad hi nhi hoga ab to pehchaane se bhi inkaar kiya hoga.

KUMAR: aisi baat bilkul bhi nhi hai, yeh to tum bhi maante hona k Kashmir main aapke aadmiyu ke haathu bahut aam civilians maare gaye hai ,ab aapke kehne pe maare ya apni marzi se itne logu ko maara lekin zimedaari to aapki thi k nhi, Aur jabse aap Kashmir main Surrender kiye the tab se India main Teen baar Prime minister badal chuke hai yeh bhi to khayal rahe. Ab aapki safety pehle dekhni hain uske baad, kyunki ab aap waise militants ke khilaaf ladte the ab waisa bhi nhi hosakta Kashmir main ab PDP ne hukumat ikhtiyaar ki hai woh yeh sab bilkul bardaash karne walu main se nhi hai. Ab aap apna khayal rakho main shayad yahan phirse na aavu mujhe baaki kaam hai bahut. Baaki aapki security main ab aur log shaamil kiye jayenge usski ijazat maine Prime Minister se le li hai.

Chalo main chalta hu ab baaki apna khayal rakho.

Kumar left like always disappeared in crowd like air.

KUKA was very worried about his family and his men who were getting killed day by day, he had no choice left other than being silent. Here in Bandipora main areas the militancy had captured speed, every other day they would through a grenade or attack on Army vehicles in answer Army would continuously go for encounters, this all was repeating again like last ten years had started spinning the wheel again.

Here Mohamad Akbar lone entered into assembly and started digging on what ikhawani's had done with civilians. This was gaining him sympathy among people so all other parties would agree on it, because technically democracy had returned to Kashmir so it was about the people now they are now the ones who are going to vote.

By the time KUKA and his men did not feel that they are being aided by Central Government, they would not feel it because the current government in India was not in favour or recognising the sacrifices KUKA had done for the cause of Kashmir being of India. So it was obviously looking like a lost situation, after few days of Kumar's and KUKA Parray's meeting Hizbul Mujahideen killed two more ex Ikhwani's in Hajan which created panic in area as people were afraid of the return of 90's militancy, everyone from the Hajan village was afraid because by the time KUKA ruled the area approximately from last ten years everyone had got involved whether directly or indirectly with KUKA parray they were afraid that Hizbul Mujahideen militants would kill them in revenge of last ten years. So now complications had raised for KUKA from everywhere, National conference leaders like Mohammad Akbar lone and Farooq Abdullah were targeting vote bank on the name of KUKA Parray and wanted him to be in jail other side Hizbul Mujahideen Militants were behind every Ikhwani and behind every one who ever supported them.

After all this life under the fear, KUKA and his men would try avoid being in public gathering as much as possible. Now KUKA started realizing what he and his men have done to the Kashmiri people, He himself was also a man who would do a lot of charity when he was MLA whoever no matter whoever would come to his residence KUKA would always keep his hands open for help and that was one thing he was proud of and that was the exact reason why some people would always support him no matter what he had done, He provided government jobs to hundreds those families would never forget his favour through their life time. But there was one interesting which had happened that whoever the people who took the most benefit from KUKA's name looted people on his name everyone had left Parray and joined other parties like national conference and people's democratic party and those were the exact people who were giving speeches in rallies against KUKA Parray, I think that what is the proper definition of politics, if said like that gangsters are more loyal to their companions and leaders then a political party workers to their leaders they just switch sides when they see the power is going to someone else.

Some months went like that and pressure was increasing from every corner. Finally KUKA's close men including his advisors called a meeting at his residence regarding the future and ways to tackle with current situation. Because safety of everyone was also a big priority.

KUKA and all other his close ones gathered in room.

Advisor to Parray: Parray ab kya karna kuch bolo roz roz aise apne logun ko marte huve to nhi dekhsakte. Yahan hindustaani Government ne bhi haath uthaya hai who to hum ko pehchaane se bhi ab inkar karenge.

Second person sitting next to Parray: Parray yeh bilkul sahi keh raha hai Hizbul Mujahideen bhi ab zor pakad rha hai Kashmir main teezi se hum kitne din aise unse chup sakenge.

Third person: Parray mujhe lagta ab hame bas apni mout ka intizaar karna hai aur kuch nhi, kyunki aur koi rasta nazar nhi aarha hai.

KUKA: Mujhe sab pata hai meri baat chal rhi hai Hindustani hukumat se iska kuch ka kuch hal zarur niklega. Aur rahi baat baaki political parties ki jo hamare liye roz assembly main hangama karte hai hamari saza ki maang kar rhe hai, woh sab siyasi nizam hai woh sab waise hi chalta hai, ek baar hum phirse election ke liye khade hojayenge aur jeet gaye to sab bhool jayenge yeh sab.

Advisor to Parray: Konse Hindustani hukumat ki baat kar rhe hai aap, wahi jisse hamara koi ehsaan tak yaad nhi hai hum nhi hote to ab tak Hizbul Mujahideen ne Kashmir pe kabza karliya hota aur Sallah ud din Srinagar ke assembly main betha hota. Aur rahi baat Hamari madad karne ki woh to nhi karne wali yeh hukumat, Hindustan ke baaki states main dange ho rhe hai woh is waqt apne logun ko bacha rhe hai unhe hamari koi parwa nhi hai.

KUKA: Aisa nhi hai is ka kuch na kuch Hal zarur niklega siyasi daaw pech hai kuch alag se sochke ke is masle so suljana hoga.

Advisor to Parray: khaali siyasi khel hota to koi baat nh9i hoti aaj ek election haarte kal phirse jeet lete, lekin yahan masla hai kuch 1000 qatal usko kaise sambalenge. Woh to hum pe ilzaam lagte aaye hai aaj nhi to kal kanooni karawayi bhi hogi uske baad kya hum sab faansi ke takhte pe honge. aur ha jis hindustaani hukumat ki aap barusa kare bethe ho woh khud taqreer denge k KUKA Parray ne civilians ko maara usko uski saza mili aur kuch nhi. Udr yeh koi nhi sochne wala zyada tar jo bhi is waqt opposition parties main is waqt hamari saza ki maang kar rhe hai zyada tar aam logu ko unhone hi sataya aur maara hai KUKA ke naam pe.

KUKA: Theek hai mujhe sochne do is baare main kuch hal nikalta hu aur main koshish karta hu sambalne ki.

Everyone left and Parray also pushed off from room, but these days he would mostly sit at home only.

Days passed situation was getting better in Kashmir but worse for KUKA and his ex ikhwani's now Hizbul Mujahideen was not targeting civilians like they did in 90's now they were targeting the ex ikhwani's and they would find them and kill them one by one no matter if anyone has dropped the weapons they were still a target, it's said that almost more than 500 militants were killed by ikhwani's till the date, and Hizbul mujahideen was taking revenge for that.

A month later due to ongoing opposition everywhere for KUKA and his outfit Ikhwan was getting blamed people also had started talking openly and the stories of ikhwan's cruelty was coming out and that would make people hate them more there was no path which could be seen for KUKA and his mens safety as it was getting worse.

Before just some days Hizbul Mujahideen Militants had opened fire at Parray's house in midnight almost 30 minutes they continued firing at his walls, may be it was just the warning for parray or a message that they were going to kill him but nobody got hurt, the CRPF troops allocated at Parray's house also firing a lot of rounds in answer but no one was hurt.

So they called the meeting again to discuss and decide what are the steps they going to take for the safety and progress of the Awami League Party.

KUKA and all other important people of Awami League gathered in room again.

Advisor to Parray: Aap ne bola tha aap baat karenge halaat theek honge jab se humne pichli baar yeh baat ki thi tab se aur 5 log maare jachuke hai ab hum kiska intezaar kar rhe hai, jab Hizbul mujahideen ke log hamare sab logu ko ek ek karke maar daale, aapke ghr pe bhi to hamla huva hai, yeh to shukar hai k kisi ko kuch nhi huva.

Second person: Haa Parray yeh theek keh raha hai hum kis ka intizaar kar rhe hai sab ke maarne ka. Aap ne bola tha aap Hindustani hukumat se baat karenge uska kya huva.

KUKA: maine sab se baat karne ki koshish ki lekin koi fayda nhi Hindustan ko ab hamari zarurat nhi hai kuch khaas, isliye kuch farak nhi padta unko.

Advisor to Parray: Parray ek baat bolu agar sab maane, mujhe lagta hai ab hamare paas koi raasta nhi bacha nhi hai, hamari wajah se Kashmiriyu ne bale hi unko Hizbul Mujahideen se chuthkara mila par bahut barbaadi dekhi, Ikhawan main hamare kuch commanders ne civil killing ki hamse bina pooche hathyaar ke nashe main uske baad Kashmiri log hame kabhi maanf nhi karenge.

KUKA: to aap kenhna kya chahte hai k hamare log jinke liye hamne itna kuch kiya woh hame apnayenge nhi, humpe agle election main barusa nhi karenge.

Advisor to Parray: agle election agar hum bache to hi woh dekhenge na, yahan Hizbul Mujahideen apni tedaad din ba din badata hi jarha hai aur wahan salahu din intizaar kar rha hai KUKA parray ke Marne ka taki woh Kashmir ko Pakistan se ila sake. Khair woh ti mumkin nhi hai ab jitni fauj Hindustan ne Kashmir main rakhi hai uss hisaab se to mumkin nhi hai. Mujhe lagta don uke donu Kashmir ki barbaadi hi chahte hai Hindustan bhi aur Pakistan bhi, Sab ko apna hi matlb dikh rha hai koi Kashmiri log uke baare main sochta tak nhi hai.

KUKA: to aap ke hisaab hamare liye kya karna munasib rahega iss waqt mujhse pooch to muje kisi pe ab barusa nhi hai sab apna fayda leke chod dete hai.

Advisor to Parray: mujhe lagta hai Pakistan to hamara dushman hamesha se tha hi lekin ab Hindustan ne bhi saabit kiya unko humse itna hi matlab tha k Kashmir main election bahaal ho aur woh united Nations ke saamne dikha sake k Kashmir khush hai India ke saath hai ,elections main participate kar rhe hai, baaki hum logu ko kal woh bhi Marwa sakte hai un pe koi barusa nhi rha ab. Kal ko hame maarke bolenge yeh logu ne Pakistan ke kehne pe Kashmir ke am logu ko maara, yahan apni hamdardi lene ke liye woh aisa karsakte hai.

KUKA: tum saaf saaf kyu hi kehte k karna kya hai, hamne isse bure halaat pehle bhi dekhe hai aur humne usko badal diya tha yaad nhi hai kya.

Advisor to Parray: Parray mujhe lagta hai hamari wajah se hamare apne logu ko bahut takleef huvi jiss Kashmir ki azaadi ke liye aap ne bandook uthayi thi, hamare logu log uke haathu wahi Kashmiri janwaru ki tarah sadku pe mare hai, Fayaz Nawbadi ne to bachu aur aurtu ko tak bhi nhi choda tha, woh usne apne pagalpanti main kiya lekin naam to Ikhwan ka hi tha, ab mujhe lagta hume Kashmir aur kashmiyu ke liye kuch karna chahiye unke liye khada hona chahiye wapas. Unhone bahut zulum dekhe chahe hamari tanzeem se ya Hizbul Mujahideen se.

Kyun na hum Kashmir ki azaadi ke liye phirse khade ho jaye jab k ab hamare samne donu mulku ka asli chehra saamne aaya hai. Sabko Kashmir chahiye, chahe uske liye kashmiriyu ka khoon paani ki tarah kyu na bahe.

KUKA: jo tum keh rahe woh itna asaan nhi hai jitna tum samajte ho.

Advisor to Parray: pata hai lekin aap yeh bhool rhe hai k aap KUKA Parray hai jab Hindustan ki Army Kashmir main haar chuki thi militants se tab aapne akele Kashmir ko unse bachaya tha. Hindustan aur Pakistan aapke naam se darr jaate hai, ab to unko pata hai aap kya karsakte hai aadi jung to hum uss darr ki wajah se hi jeet jayenge.

KUKA: yeh phir bhi itna asaan nhi hai main sochta hu iske baare main phir bolunga.

Everyone left and went while putting Parray in deep thinking what his one of the advisor had said.

As days passed it right before some days of next meeting, there was a cricket Match going on in sports ground Hajan so KUKA was called as chief guest and to honour the final winners with the wining CUP. It was Saturday 13 September 2003 when time once again turned the tide.

Parray was going in his Geep to sports after lunch when he was attacked by two Unknown gun men's every News Paper and every organisation published there perspectives about Parray's life and Death. just after few days of the meeting of KUKA with his associates and this happened. next day according to telegraph News was like:

"Kuka Parray, the father of the counter-insurgency movement in Kashmir, was killed in an audacious militant strike on the third blood-splattered Saturday in the state in a row.

Mohammad Yousuf Parray aka Kuka Parray was on his way to a school compound for a cricket match, where he was to be the chief guest, when militants ambushed his vehicle in Hajan village,

In a rash of attacks, three army jawans and a major were killed in an early morning *fidayeen* strike on an army camp near the Line of Control in Kupwara and two civilians died in a mine blast on the Srinagar-Jammu National Highway.

"Kuka Parray was the symbol of counter-insurgency, his death is a major blow to the security forces in their fight against terror. It will raise the morale of militants who had tried unsuccessfully to get him several times," a senior bureaucrat in Delhi acknowledged. Police in Srinagar described the killing as a serious setback.

Just over two weeks ago, Parray's close associate, Javed Ahmad Shah, was killed in a suicide strike in Srinagar while Prime Minister Atal Bihari Vajpayee, his cabinet colleagues and several chief ministers were in town.

"The militants first hurled a hand-grenade on the vehicle and later sprayed bullets from their automatic weapons," a senior police officer said. "The attack was so swift that the police guards of Parray could not return the fire."

Police were aware Parray would be targeted after Javed was killed as militants tried to disprove Delhi's claim that normality was returning under chief minister Mufti Mohammad Sayeed.

The counter-insurgent and seven others were critically injured and taken to the hospital in the nearby army camp. Parray and two of his associates died even as efforts were on to rush them to Srinagar. The body was taken to his home in the village.

Parray and Javed were credited with "turning around the situation in the Valley at the height of militancy". Police officers in Srinagar privately admit that without the two, the 1996 elections — held after a gap of seven years — would not have been possible.

The Kashmiri folk singer, who made a living out of performing at weddings before becoming a militant, left the separatist ranks in 1995 and founded his pro-India militant outfit, Ikhwan-ul Muslemoon.

Parray's death will hit the morale of the Ikhwanis — the surrendered militants who flocked to him for protection and helped the security forces — and seriously affect the flow of information on militants at a time when violence has renewed.

Tension gripped Hajan after the attack on Parray at the main *chowk*. Senior state officials, including Kashmir divisional commissioner Parvez Dewan, who were inside the cricket ground, were escorted to Srinagar. The al-Nasiree and the Kashmir Freedom Force have admitted responsibility for Parray's killing.

Today was the third violent Saturday in a row — Gazi Baba, the Jaish-e-Mohammad chief in the Valley, was gunned down on August 30 and a car bomb in Srinagar killed seven on September 6."

The most Shocking and confusing thing about the incident was that outfit who claimed the responsibility of these killings was The al-Nasiree. One one had heard the name of this outfit till the date who were they what was there aim and why they killed, Hizbul Mujahideen had enough reasons to kill Parray which they could do easily but why they didn't do that, why The al-Nasiree outfit had to do it, those were some unanswered questions which no one could answer surely.

According to Indian government he was killed by this outfit who was a pro Pakistani outfit linked with Hizbul mujahideen and they took the revenge from Parray, but locals of Kashmir and people who were linked with him still believes that the RAW had got info about the meeting and they couldn't afford it if KUKA Parray would have turned Sides again.

The killing of KUKA Parray left many questions behind, would have Parray changed the side and gone once again against Indian army and Government or he would still decide to fight elections and live life democratically. After that the Kashmir issue still stays unresolved and Gorilla force have still presence in Kashmir, Kashmiris also have to live with more than 1.3 million Indian troops in the valley. And the story continues…

Bibliography

- Kashmir life articles "Ikhwan tales"
- Wikipedia "Kashmir History"
- Adi Magazine "A historical timeline"
- The Telegraph article
- University of Central Arkansas
- The Carter Centre
- The Rediff.com
- Frontline.thehindu.com
- The wire
- Kashmirpost.org
- Outlookindia.com
- Britannica.com
- Human rights watch organisation
- Theprint.in
- Quora.com
- Youtube.com/Nitish Rajput
- Wikiwand.com
- Therealkashmir.com
- Freepresskashmir.news
- Economictimes.com

- Greaterkashmir.com
- Youtube.com/ndtv
- Standwithkashmir.medium.com
- Bloodiedrivers.wordpress.com
- Mumbaimirror.indiatimes.com

www.ingramcontent.com/pod-product-compliance
Lightning Source LLC
LaVergne TN
LVHW061616070526
838199LV00078B/7304